THE BALTIMORE CLIPPER

BALTIMORE CLIPPER PRIVATEER SCHOONER
From an oil painting by Burton (1815) in the Macpherson Collection

THE
BALTIMORE CLIPPER

ITS

ORIGIN AND DEVELOPMENT

By Howard Irving Chapelle

BONANZA BOOKS · NEW YORK

PREFACE

THIS book has been written with a sincere admiration for the Baltimore Clipper, yet with a fairly clear comprehension of its faults. In recent years little has been published, from a technical standpoint, about the old types of ships and it is hoped that the model builder and the antiquarian may find the following study of value. If one were to build a Baltimore Clipper, privateer or slaver, at the present time, what elements of design would be necessary? In the following pages a sincere effort has been made to answer this question.

To Prof. E. P. Morris of Saybrook, Connecticut, belongs much of the credit for this volume, he having made the suggestion that plans being brought together merely as a private collection be incorporated in a book on the subject. Before reproducing these plans they were carefully redrawn so that they might be reproduced clearly and also to aid in visualizing the points of design. The inboard and outboard profiles are superimposed in the original draughts and in redrawing, these plans have been separated to avoid confusion. Where reconstruction was necessary it has been indicated.

I am greatly indebted to Mr. C. Knight, the British Admiralty Curator, for his long and laborious search in the Admiralty archives for plans of small sailing craft, some of which are reproduced in this book. From him came the plans of privateers and also of the slaver. To members and also to the Secretary of the Admiralty Board, I am indebted for the necessary permission to reproduce these plans in the Admiralty Collection. Mr. Basil Lubbock has been most helpful and has contributed much valuable information. Many interesting articles by Mr. Charles G. Davis and Mr. C. H. J. Snyder, published in yachting magazines, have been consulted and much of value in connection with the Baltimore Clipper has been found in books written by them.

HOWARD IRVING CHAPELLE.

Boston, Massachusetts
    August 9, 1930

CONTENTS

PLATES

PLANS

xi

THE BALTIMORE CLIPPER

CHAPTER I

THE BALTIMORE CLIPPER

THERE is no type of vessel that has so much romantic and historical interest to Americans as that commonly called the Baltimore
Clipper. First appearing in naval history during the war of the
Revolution, the type soon became famous. By 1800 the Baltimore Clipper
was extremely popular with privateers, slavers and other mariners requir-
ing fast vessels.

It would be impossible to write a history of American privateering, the
slave trade, or even of piracy, without mention of this type of vessel. The
"rakish topsail schooner" is so often mentioned in the voyages of the mariners of the early nineteenth century, that one's curiosity cannot but be
aroused as to the history and appearance of these craft. Generally schooner-rigged, they were often engaged in illegal trades — in smuggling in the
West Indies and in piracy. Illicit and desperate practices followed close in
their wakes throughout their existence.

The chief characteristics of these craft were long, light, and extremely
raking masts; very little rigging; low freeboard; great rake to stem and
stern posts, with a great deal of drag to the keel, aft. Their deadrise was
great and bilges slack. The beam was usually rather great for their length.
Nearly always flush-decked, they had wide, clear decks, suitable for working the ships and handling the guns. When engaged in privateering they
often had high bulwarks, particularly in vessels of the larger class.

It is rather strange, considering the popularity of this type, that so little
has been written about them. The clipper ships of the '50's were no more
popular with mariners of that date than were the Baltimore Clippers with
the seamen of the early nineteenth century, yet there is a wealth of material on the clipper ship and almost nothing on the Baltimore Clippers.
There are but two books that give much material, both written abroad.
The most important is Marestier's book, "Memoirs sur les bateaux a vapeur des Etats Unis," published in France in 1822. This contains eight
plans, but none of them show any great amount of detail. They have been
redrawn and partly reconstructed for this work. The other book is Knowles'

3

"Naval Architecture," London, 1822. This contains two plans, probably reprints from Steele's earlier book of about 1806. These plans show more detail and have been redrawn and are here included. They will be discussed

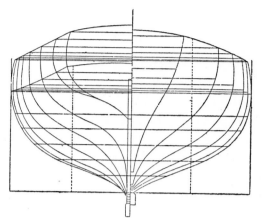

FIG. 1 — LINES OF THE FRENCH LUGGER "LE COUREUR"

later. Fortunately we have found a number of plans in the English Royal Navy Collections, and through the kindness of the curator, Mr. C. Knight, we are able to offer them as evidence of the beauty and excellence of the Baltimore Clippers.

The most important thing, in beginning our study, is the parent type, or, at least, the influence that brought forth these famous craft. The design of this type is commonly ascribed to French models, particularly the fast luggers, a few of which came over during the Revolution. The plan of one of these luggers, *Le Coureur*, is reproduced here. This identical vessel is known to have been on the American coast during the Revolution and her plan is taken from Paris' "Souvenirs de Marine," Vol. I. It represents a three-masted lugger of the chasse maree type, built in 1776. She was built by M. Denys and the plan was approved by M. de Santune, minister of the Marine, and the order for her construction was signed December 22, 1775.

This type, Admiral Paris states, was not mentioned in French naval history before 1778. His note on this particular vessel includes the fact that she took part in the battle of Belle-Poule, under the command of Chevalier Rosily, and that she was on the American coast during the Revolution.

This is a remarkably fine plan of the lugger type, showing deck profile, as well as lines and rig. Attention is called to the raised quarter-deck and half ports, which apparently were common in these vessels. The lines show a powerful and fast craft with slightly raking ends, great deadrise and rather sharp waterlines. She was heavily sparred and canvased; her bowsprit was a tremendous spar and characteristic of the type.

A comparison of this plan with those of the Baltimore type, shown throughout this book, cannot but cause one to question the theory of the influence of the French on the design. With the exception of the midship section there is almost no similarity. The stern and stem posts are more upright, the design of the ends differs in section and of course there is no likeness in rig. Moreover, as one weighs the evidence of the conservatism of seamen and ship-builders, it is difficult to believe that in the comparatively short time between the beginning and end of the Revolution, particularly during France's participation therein, that a type so different from the standard vessels of that date should become popular.

It should be added that there is, however, some evidence of French influence. Whether or not this was in the design or construction must always remain a matter of opinion. It is the writer's belief that this influence was in construction and finish, but not in design. The following advertisement is offered as evidence, but of course is not conclusive.

New Vessel for Sale

A new vessel. Burthen 136 tons, of pilot-boat construction, built at Baltimore and launched the latter part of last month. She is built with live-oak and cedar, nailed and finished after the French manner, being calculated for extraordinary sailing.

This vessel is masted as a schooner, with topmast, yards, sails, anchors, cables, rigging and every other material, all new and of the best quality. She is entirely ready for receiving a cargo, and may be viewed at Mr. Pascault's wharf, at the Point, where she now lays. If not sold privately before Monday the 22nd June, she will then be exposed for sale by public auction, on that day. Apply to Messrs. Casinove and Walker, in Water Street, for further particulars.—*Maryland Journal and Baltimore Universal Daily Advertiser*, June 17, 1795.

It is possible that the influence of the French on these craft was felt prior to the Revolution. The naval histories of wars between England and France, prior to 1775, fail to show, however, how such influence reached Baltimore. While the type could not have sprung into being without outside influence, it is difficult to believe that it was solely due to the copying of French models during the Revolution.

As it has often been stated that the Continental frigates, *Hancock*, *Trumbull*, *Raleigh*, *Confederacy*, *Virginia*, etc., were built on French models, as were the *Constitution* and *Constellation* of later date, it is highly probable that these references have been confused and applied to the Baltimore craft as well.

There was doubtless some application of French construction and finish after the Revolution, as the builders became aware of the excellence of the French vessels. But the influence on the design does not appear to be great. Deadrise was not the sole property of the French luggers, as the cutter of the English, and the Jamaica sloop in the West Indies, as well as other types,

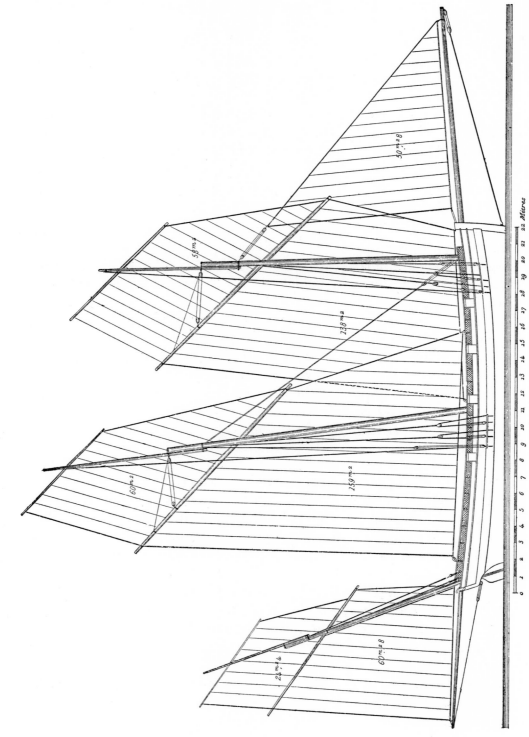

SAIL PLAN OF THE FRENCH LUGGER "LE COUREUR," OF 1775

From Admiral de Paris, "Souvenirs de Marine," Vol. I

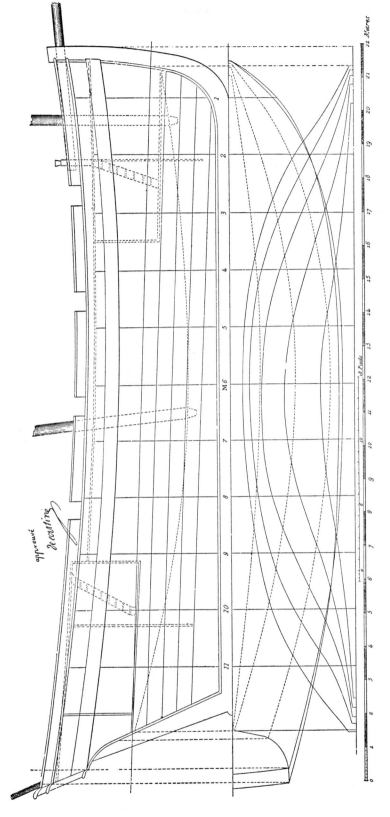

approuvé
Recentive

INBOARD PROFILE AND LINES OF THE FRENCH LUGGER "LE COUREUR," OF 1775
From Admiral de Paris, "Souvenirs de Marine," Vol. I

had this element of speed. In fact it is extremely difficult, putting aside a speculation of possibilities, to find much comparison between the lugger and the clipper.

If any xebecs or other Mediterranean craft were in American waters during the period just prior to the Revolution, there would be some cause to ascribe the design of the Baltimore vessels to their influence. Certainly the Baltimore vessels showed more likeness to the xebec or galley than to the lugger. The ends of the clippers had much the same profile as the xebec and the modern Baltimore and Chesapeake craft show even a stronger resemblance.

So far nothing has been found to connect the American type with that of the Mediterranean. It is barely possible that such evidence may be found in the future, but it is very doubtful. If there were any such influences they may have come through the West Indies and the Spanish Colonies, particularly Cuba. Spain built a large number of small war vessels at an early date in Habana, and some of these may have ventured northward and become models for the builders on the Chesapeake, prior to the Revolution.

There is another theory that Mr. Charles G. Davis advanced in an article in the American yachting magazine "Yachting." In an article on Marestier's plans, he suggested that the Baltimore Clipper descended from the Swedish fishing craft built by the early Swedish settlers of the country about Baltimore. Apparently he based his theory on the coincidence of their early settlement in this district, as well as a marked similarity in lines and appearance of the Baltimore Clipper to the Swedish and other Scandinavian vessels. This appears quite possible and is worthy of more credence than the theory of French influence. While there is no documentary evidence to back Mr. Davis' theory, there is, at least, a possibility of these Swedish fishing craft having been adapted for Chesapeake waters and finally evolved into the Baltimore Clipper.

Of these various possibilities the reader may make his choice, but all of them leave much to be desired in the matter of proof. From these theories there can be little visible evidence of the various changes in design that must have taken place.

There is also another possibility; when buccaneering became popular in the West Indies, there were very few types of small, fast vessels in use. The requirements of these gentle mariners were speed, for chasing and escaping; ability to carry guns, though the buccaneers trusted largely to boarding; small size, due to the necessity of hiding behind cays and in mangrove swamps; and room for large crews. Their larger ships were the smaller galleons and frigates of their day and captured merchant vessels that were either very large and strong or quite fast. They soon developed, however, a class of small sloops called Jamaica sloops. These were popular in the West Indies previous to 1725, apparently, and are pictured in old prints as having square topsails, long bowsprits and loose-footed gaff mainsails.

These vessels, while small, were very popular with the smaller bands of buccaneers, and later with the West Indian pirates. Not only were they used in piracy and intermittent warfare, but also in trade, particularly the smuggling trade with the Spanish Colonies. All these trades, in fact, any trade in the West Indies during this lawless period, necessitated a fast and handy craft. These stringent requirements were filled quite well by the Jamaica sloop. Even the Royal Navy adopted them for small cruisers, during the early eighteenth century. As this type became popular and as the ship-builders of other of the West Indian islands became acquainted with the design, the Jamaica sloop began to be built over a large area and eventually the building of this type spread to Bermuda.

During the early period of the occupation of Bermuda the chief business of the islands was ship-building. Because of the wealth of timber, a good grade of cedar, and the natural aptitude of her people, Bermuda soon became the leading ship-building community in American waters. At this time the buccaneers and pirates were demanding the Jamaica type, as were other mariners and traders in the West Indies, so it came about that Bermudians became the leading builders of the Jamaica type. In fact, by 1750, the name "Jamaica sloop" was not often applied, and the type had become the "Bermuda sloop."

This new type apparently was merely an improvement of the Jamaica sloop. During the transition period, the two names were applied at the same time. One often comes across old prints showing "A Jamaica or Bermuda Sloop." This double naming apparently existed for many years, but finally the type became merely the "Bermuda sloop."

The Bermuda sloop retained the popularity of the earlier Jamaica vessels, and had the same characteristics. They were far ahead of the times in design, and though small, were rivals of the Baltimore Clippers in the slave trade, at a later date, particularly in Brazil. During the period of their existence they were always used in trades or in business demanding fast, weatherly craft, suitable for smuggling and warfare and it must be remembered that the Baltimore Clippers were subject to the same stringent demands.

The next point that may be brought forward, is the commercial intercourse between Bermuda and Virginia and the Chesapeake. Prof. E. P. Morris in his recent book, "The History of the Fore and Aft Rig in America," has gone into a wealth of detail and consulted a great number of authorities in proof of the constant intercourse between the two colonies during the early period of their history. From this one can see that there is a strong possibility that the Baltimore Clipper descended from the Jamaica sloop, by way of Bermuda. It appears highly probable that the Chesapeake Bay builders saw and copied the vessels of the Bermudians, as they found a need for having fast vessels.

The Bermuda sloop was far in advance of the other classes of vessels of her period. At all times the Bermuda sloop showed an improved design. In 1806 they had begun to rocker the keel and they kept pace with all improvements in naval architecture during the whole of their existence.

Fortunately we have available a plan of the early Bermuda sloop. It is found in Chapman's "Navalis Architecturia Mercatoria," printed about 1782. This plan is probably of a vessel built about 1750 and shows the type of this sloop just prior to the first appearance of the Baltimore Clipper in naval history. A comparison of the lines of this vessel with that of the Baltimore Clipper shows a remarkable resemblance. The Bermuda sloop of 1750 had very raking stern and stem post, low freeboard, raking mast and much deadrise. The beam was large and the vessel drew a great deal of water. These elements can be seen in the drawing and with the exception of the high stern, there was little change, other than minor improvements, in this type until the early nineteenth century.

The spar lengths of the sloop are given in Chapman, so it is possible to reconstruct a sail plan. The square topsails seem very small, and the head sails very large, but apparently this was common in most sloops of that date. Her spars were heavy and the rig appears extremely large. The rake of the mast was extreme and not duplicated in other craft of that date.

In comparing the Baltimore Clipper with the Bermudian, the rake of the ends, and general shape of the bow-sections, show some similarity. The deep drag of the keel and the shape of the mid-section show even stronger likeness. The general underbody profile, low freeboard and rake to the spars appears common to both types. While no deck plans of the Bermudian sloop exist, they probably differed little from the clippers in this respect.

There is still more to be said concerning the possibility of the Baltimore type having descended from the Jamaica and Bermuda sloop. While keeping in mind the commercial and political conditions that produced the Jamaica sloop let us consider the conditions that brought about the production of the Baltimore Clipper.

During the entire eighteenth century the leading nations of Europe were engaged in war. The bitter enmity of France and Great Britain were among

VIEW OF THE TOWN AND HARBOUR OF MONTEGO BAY, JAMAICA

Showing the shipping in the year 1770. From an engraving in the Macpherson Collection

A BERMUDA SCHOONER IN 1834

From a water color by J. Lynn, in the Macpherson Collection

VIEW OF NASSAU IN THE BAHAMAS, SHOWING A BAHAMAN SCHOONER

From a drawing by N. Pocock, after drawings by Capt. Piercy Frazer
Reproduced from a mezzotint in the "Naval Chronicle," Vol. 2 (1799)

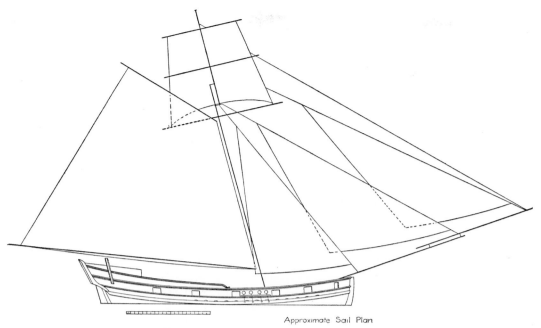

Approximate Sail Plan

BERMUDA SLOOP — FROM CHAPMAN

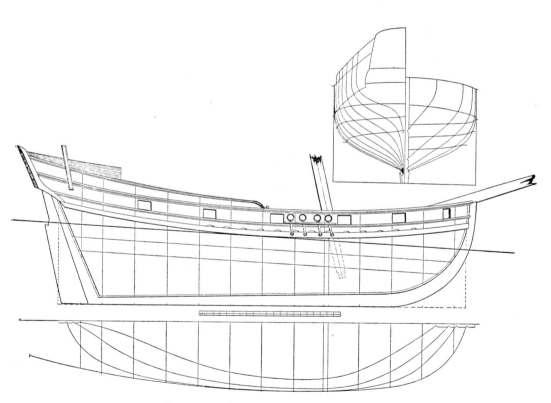

BERMUDA SLOOP — FROM CHAPMAN

Length between perpendiculårs	60′ 9″
Beam moulded	21′ 2″
Draught of water	12′ 3″

Ten 4-pounders (carriage guns) and 12 swivels

the causes of this condition and the intrigues and politics of the period served to bring into conflict Spain, France, England and Holland, all seafaring nations, with the natural result that all commerce at sea was very hazardous, and liable to loss through seizure by war vessels of the contending powers. The American Colonies, being English possessions, had to contend with both France and Spain in the Western Atlantic. Constant pressure was also brought to bear on the Colonies, by the Mother Country, to suppress their trade, particularly with the West Indies and the Spanish possessions. As the trade of the American Colonies threatened to become important, the Navigation Laws were rigidly enforced by England, and so another obstacle was thrown in the way of the American mariner and trader.

Large vessels were not needed by the Colonies, as cargoes were not large; a seaport town could not produce many manufactures nor much raw material in those days. Nor could the shipowners build large vessels due to the economic conditions. The wars abroad, the Indian troubles at home, and the damage to their sea-borne trade all combined to keep the Colonies in more or less poverty.

If a shipowner expected to make money, in nearly all trades, he had to have a vessel fast enough to escape the cruisers of the combatants, and well enough armed to beat off petty pirates, and even the smaller war vessels.

The Baltimore builders having these conditions before them, and with increasing demands for speed and power in small vessels from the shipowners, may have turned to the type with which they had become acquainted through their neighbors, the Bermudians. This would be natural as the Bermuda sloops visited the Chesapeake often and were no doubt carefully studied by the Baltimore builders. Since also, the type nearly filled the wants of the American shipowners, these builders probably took over the design bodily at first, and then began to improve upon it.

The largest of the Bermuda sloops were about seventy feet on deck, and were large for one-masted vessels. Their crews were necessarily large. In the Baltimore type, due to economic reasons, it was necessary to keep the crew less numerous, so probably this introduced the schooner rig. Furthermore, weatherliness being a necessity, the square rig was out of the question. The ability to escape to windward was an absolute necessity in a small vessel, as she would usually be overpowered by the large vessel in strong winds on any other course. This, then, ruled out the favorite brig rig of that time, as well as the ketch. We may then safely assume that they adopted the New England pinky rig and applied it to the transplanted Bermudian sloop.

Another reason for the popularity of the schooner rig was the lack of weight aloft and the small amount of rigging required in the early examples of the schooner rig as is seen in old prints. These early, schooner-rigged vessels were lightly sparred and carried very little top hamper and this light rigging remained one of the characteristics of the Baltimore Clipper for quite a period; in the schooners, at least.

In the privateers, slavers, and pirates, there was one tactic that they used at night, when chased, or in attacking. It was particularly useful on starlight nights when there was little wind. Then they would drop their sails and use sweeps to creep away from an enemy, or to surprise a merchantman. There was no loom of sails against the stars, nor were there large tops and masses of rigging to show in the starlight.

The use of sweeps in the Baltimore Clippers was very common. The oarports were between the gun-ports, as a rule. This method of propulsion was popular with American privateersmen during the War of 1812 and later with the slavers. Of course they would only be used in small vessels with large crews.

It is unnecessary at this point to give an account of the schooner rig. There is so much in doubt that an attempt to trace the various changes in rig is almost hopeless as the whole matter seems to be one of opinion and will probably remain so. However, it will perhaps be safe to assume that the Baltimore builders were acquainted with the development of the rig in New England. As early as Feb. 11, 1717, the *Schooner Ann* was recorded in the marine news of the "Boston News-Letter," as bound outward for South Carolina and five months later the *Schooner Dalphin*, was outward bound for the Barbadoes. In November of the same year, a schooner from Boston and another belonging to London, England, were captured by pirates on the North Carolina coast. Trade with the West Indies was always large and active, and naturally would bring New England vessels into frequent intercourse with the Baltimore people. Their builders would quickly see the possibilities of such a rig when applied to their large sloops and would adopt it.

The types which were most common in New England during the early period were the Chebacco and dogbody boats and later, the pinky and topsail schooner. The Baltimore builders would quickly see that it was possible to increase the length of their vessels with a two-masted rig like that of the New Englanders, and soon found that this length also increased the speed of their craft. Of still greater importance was the lower cost of upkeep of the rig when compared with the sloop.

The sloop had to have a larger crew as well as heavier spars and gear, an additional cost which, in the eyes of the Baltimore builders, might better be put into length. Perhaps, too, the shallower waters in Chesapeake Bay may have induced the local builders to cut down draft thereby losing the stability and power necessary for the large sloop rig.

If our suppositions are correct, the Maryland builders soon adopted the schooner rig and from that time on the Baltimore Clipper became a new and distinct class of vessel. No date can be definitely assigned to this change, but it would probably be between 1730 and 1750.

When we have considered the similarity of the Bermuda sloop and the Baltimore Clipper, with their commercial relationship and the possibilities of a natural development, the theory, here advanced, seems more satisfactory than any of the others that have been mentioned. At least, we are able to trace a possible evolution, with plans and historical facts to back up our assumptions and speculations on the development of the type.

All this, however, must remain for the present, at least, a matter of opinion. It is possible that more satisfactory data exists in the archives of the British Admiralty or the French and Spanish Navies. If access could be had to these sources, much more in the possible development of the clipper might be brought to light. The situation, as it is at present, leads us to believe that the Baltimore Clipper first became noticed and admired during the Revolution.

The question of the parent type has had, at least, a complete review. While there remain many points in doubt, particularly as to dates, we at least can generalize on the subject with the data available. If the Baltimore Clipper antedated the Revolution, it is highly probable that she is descended from the Jamaica sloop or possibly the Swedish craft. If, however, there was no such development before the Revolution, and if the type came into being suddenly, then it would be possible to accept the theory of French influence.

The reputation of the Baltimore Clippers for speed, was always of the highest. Everything that went into their construction apparently was of the best quality. As the type began to gain a distinctive reputation, the Baltimore builders took great pride in turning out vessels of the highest class; in speed, construction, and appearance. In their search for speed, the type became more and more extreme, particularly in the matter of deadrise and draft. In the last chapter of their history, that of the slave trade, they were matched against the famous experimental brigs of the Royal Navy. These had been brought into existence by the same search for speed, and the two classes had many an exacting brush.

The reasons for the speed of the clippers are found in their design. Generally speaking, it was due to their easy lines, light weight above to load waterline, and large rig. The lines, as will be seen, are excellent, and in some cases, so far in advance of their times that there is no comparison with other vessels of the same date. Certainly the Royal Navy found out their qualities during the early nineteenth century and used their design in a number of instances, for brigs.

Further on we will discuss in detail these craft in both privateering and in the slave trade and will, perhaps, be able to visualize the "long black Baltimore model schooner" under a cloud of snowy-white canvas, reaching across the wind.

It will be well to add that the effect of this type was great on the design of small war vessels, both in the English and French Navies, but seemingly much less in the United States Navy. There were few schooners in the United States Navy at any time and this was perhaps the reason. The foreign navies, however, used the schooner a great deal during the early nineteenth century, so this may account for foreign interest in the type.

With this introduction to the type we may now pass on to the first historical mention of the Baltimore Clipper, and the vessels of the early Colonial Navy in the Revolution.

CHAPTER II

THE BALTIMORE CLIPPER DURING
THE REVOLUTION

THE Baltimore Clipper does not appear under that name during the Revolutionary War. When the war began in 1775 apparently there were very few fast vessels in the hands of the Northern Colonies. The vessels of the Southern Colonies were often referred to as "Virginia-built," and this was the name applied to the Baltimore schooner at that period of its development. These appear to have been very fast and were successful privateers, later in the war.

The first overt acts of war were committed in the New England Colonies and in the naval attacks against the custom vessels, coasting sloops and whale boats were used. During 1775, however, the Colonies began to send forth schooners and brigs against English commerce. The appearance of those early colonial craft probably did not differ greatly from those shown in Chapman's "Navalis Architectura Mercatoria." The small sloops, brigs, and schooners of New England were converted merchant vessels and fishing craft. The brigs and schooners were probably about seventy-five feet long and the sloops were smaller. Chapman's drawings show many of the large sloops and the brigs and snows of this period, no doubt like the craft mentioned.

The English employed in the custom service a large number of sloops and cutters and a few schooners. The Royal Navy had a few schooners, but the fleet in American waters was composed mostly of ships, sloops and brigs, with a few ships of the line and a number of frigates.

The colonies, due to the lack of large ships, could not wage a naval war, yet they had to have vessels to procure the munitions of war and as their ports were under blockade, it was necessary to procure and use fast ships both for trade and privateering.

That the "Virginia-built" schooners and brigs were best suited for the service required is shown in the list of privateers of the Revolution, where there is gradual increase in number and size of schooners during the latter days of the war, and the majority of the "Virginia-built" vessels are supposed to have been schooners. Many, however, were rigged as brigs, no doubt to fit them for war service. As the war progressed, however, large 10-, 16- and 20-gun schooners became popular.

In the first official navy of the Colonies we find the 8-gun schooner *Wasp* and the 8-gun schooner *Fly*. These, too, may have been "Virginia-built," as they were procured at or near Philadelphia. This was in 1775 or 1776. At the time these schooners were in service, others were borrowed from Massachusetts by General Washington to cruise in the Bay of St. Lawrence to capture the English supply ships. These were the 6-gun schooner *Lynch*, and the 4-gun schooner *Franklin*, both also having ten swivels. There were also a number of schooners belonging to the various State governments. The schooner *Defence*, of South Carolina, is mentioned as a State vessel.

The employment of schooners so early in the war would tend to show that the type was fairly numerous before 1774. These vessels were all small, perhaps fishing vessels. Schooners, later on, were most numerous, particularly among the Southern privateers. The privateers of New England and New York were largely sloops and brigs.

Some of the privateer schooners which were probably of the Baltimore type, or "Virginia-built," were the *Baltimore Hero*, 14 guns, of 1779; *Cat*, of 2 guns, 1779; *Jay*, 18 guns, 1779; *Viper*, 16 guns, 1780; and the *Scammel*, 16 guns, 1782. At the end of the war a number of these schooners were transferred to the French, among which, James, in his "Naval History of Great Britain," mentions the *Atalante* of eight guns. This schooner, under the French flag, and largely manned by Americans, was fitted out at Charleston, S. C. She probably was owned by Americans as well. She took part in an attack on an English packet ship, the *Antelope*, in 1793, and was captured.

The numerous references to schooners in early colonial history tend to carry out the theory already expressed, and it is important that we should know how the Baltimore Clipper looked during this period, when she was called "Virginia-built."

The first example of a "Virginia-built" privateer that we have, is a plate in Knowles' "Naval Architecture," London, 1822. This work is a reprint from Steel's "Naval Architecture," London, 1805, and shows, possibly, a vessel of the time of the Revolution. This vessel has the vertical guards on her bulwarks, aft, that had disappeared by 1790. Her stern, also, is higher than was common by 1800. Steel's book was published in 1805, and republished in 1812 and 1820. The stern of this craft, in spite of her size, is a square transom. This build became rare about 1800. All these details point to the supposition that this plan is of a vessel of the later part of the Revolution. Furthermore, a glance over the plans of Baltimore Clippers of 1800-

1812, show flush-decks, whereas this plan shows a raised quarter-deck. The original plate shows a trim line with less draft aft, but the waterline shown is probably accurate as to fore and aft trim. The waterlines on the original plate were probably parallel to a take-off base line, but do not represent her sailing lines. For this reason the new waterlines were drawn.

This is a very interesting craft, as from her we can piece out the probable appearance of all "Virginia-built" privateers of the later Revolutionary period. She was probably rigged as a double-topsail schooner, as she carries on her channels, the same number of deadeyes for each mast. She was armed with twelve guns, apparently. She steered with a tiller. At the stern was a small hatch opening into her run; forward of this was a cabin skylight, then a companionway at the break of the deck; next came two pump wells, one each side of the keelson; and forward of these was the mainmast. Between the main- and foremasts was a large hatch opening into the main hold and used for general purposes. Forward of the foremast was a riding bitt and a forecastle hatch. Probably there was another set of bitts and winch at the keel of the bowsprit.

This vessel was very nearly the same size as the famous United States Naval schooner *Enterprise*, of 1798. The *Enterprise*, being a much later type, differed a great deal in appearance and later she was converted into a brig. She was built at Baltimore on these general lines, however, for a fast, light cruiser.

It would be an interesting experience to stand on the deck of this "Virginia-built" privateer, to see her wide decks, and row of six guns on each side; her towering spars and lofty sails, with a crew of from 50 to 100 men crowding her decks. Yet, in imagination one can sail in her at least. As an illustration of the handling of similar vessels we may take the *Saratoga*. A member of her crew tells of the troubles of her captain when, in company with a privateer sloop, she attacked a Tory privateer, the *Dublin*. The *Saratoga* had agreed to help another Rhode Island privateer, the *Argo*, to attack the Tory vessel when she came out of New York. To encourage the English vessel, the *Argo* was to attack first and then the *Saratoga* was to come to her aid. After the *Argo* had engaged the *Dublin* for two hours, her crew began to wonder at the slowness of the *Saratoga* to come to their aid. The reason is described as follows:

"The *Saratoga* was steered with a long wooden tiller on common occasions, but in time of action the wooden tiller was unshipped and put out of the way, and she was then steered with an iron one that was shipped into the rudder head from the cabin (below deck). In the hurry of preparing for battle this iron tiller had been shoved into the opening of the rudder case,

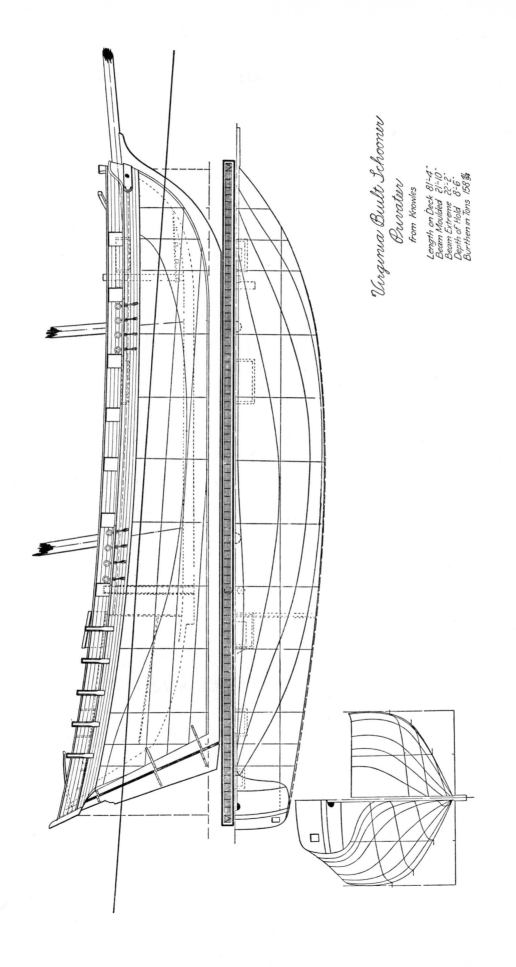

Virginia Built Schooner
Privateer
from Knowles

Length on Deck 81'-4"
Beam Moulded 21'-10"
Beam Extreme 22'-2"
Depth of Hold 8'-6"
Burthen in Tons 158 94/95

but had not entered its mortise in the rudder head at all, and the *Saratoga* went away with the wind at a smart rate, to the surprise of Captain Talbot (of the *Argo*) and the still greater surprise of Captain Munroe, who repeatedly called to the helmsman:

"'Hard a-weather, hard up there!'

"'It is hard up sir!'

"'You lie, you blackguard! She goes away lasking. Hard a-weather, I say again.'

"'It is hard a-weather indeed, sir,' was the only reply the harassed helmsman could make.

"Captain Munroe was astonished and could not conceive what the devil was the matter with his vessel! He took in her after sails and made all the headsail in his power. 'All' would not do, and away she went. He was in the utmost vexation lest Captain Talbot should think him actually running away. At last one of his officers suggested that possibly the iron tiller had not entered the rudder head, which, on examination, was found to be the case. The blunder was soon corrected and the *Saratoga* was made to stand toward the enemy, and that some satisfaction might be made for his long absence, Captain Munroe determined, as soon as he got up, to give them a whole broadside at once. He did so, and the *Dublin* immediately struck her colors."*

This narrative gives us a number of ideas as to how the smaller Revolutionary craft were handled. It seems that they carried two tillers (one a spare); one above deck, and another below (for emergency), in the cabin, aft.

Reference to the plans of the *Swift* and *Carleton* will show how this was possible, without interference. The helmsman would be protected against small arms fire, and would have to be "conned" from the deck above. Probably an officer stood at the cabin skylight, or the hatch opening into the run, and called his orders through these openings to the man at the tiller. An awkward method, but safe in close action. These below-deck tillers were used in a number of English gunbrigs built between 1800 and 1808, vessels designed for close fighting.

The handling of these schooners called for large crews, no doubt. Apparently many of them were double-topsail schooners and carried a large number of light sails. The example taken from Knowles, of a "Virginia-built" privateer, illustrates the first stage of the larger and more extreme schooners that later were called Baltimore Clippers.

* Caritat's "Life of Silas Talbot."

Fortunately we have a more complete example of the fast American craft of the later Revolutionary period. This is the schooner *Swift*. There is, it should be stated, some question as to where this vessel was built. Her decoration on the transom is the French fleur-de-lys. There is a vessel in Charnock's List of the Royal Navy (History of Marine Architecture) listed as having 14 guns, and a crew of 125 men, named *Swift*, taken from the Americans in 1779. There are also two other *Swifts* rated as sloops of war, and another as a cutter.* Furthermore, the manuscript lists of the Royal Navy state that this vessel was "taken from ye Americans." Therefore there can be no doubt that she was an American, but it is impossible to trace her original name. Probably she

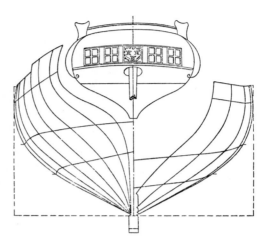

FIG. 2 — LINES OF THE SLOOP "SWIFT"

was built in the war and had a French name. There are a number of these vessels, but the data on them is so uncertain that no attempt at identification can be made.

In the drawings the *Swift* is rigged as a brig, but it seems that she was originally a schooner. This vessel varies quite a lot from the vessel in Knowles. The underbody is somewhat similar and the sections are not widely different, but the topsides and head are very different. The *Swift* is also smaller and *apparently* carried ten guns. It is to be noted that small rates carried more guns than rated, but were usually rated one port less than pierced for.

The *Swift* is a handsome vessel, more ornate than the "Virginia-built Privateer." Her stern windows have the decorated panels before mentioned; her quarters have a carved badge, around a quarter window; the carving on the badge is the usual classic leaf and scroll ornament, the main element of which is shown in the accompanying sketch. The head had either a plain billet and scroll or a short carved figure. No details of this are given and it is highly possible that a plain billet was carried. Small craft were often decorated with carved figureheads, however, and examples are numerous in Chapman's book. The constant reference here made to this work, for vessels of this period, makes it necessary to add that the New York Public Library has a copy of this rare book, and photostat copies of the plates

* *Swift*, ship-sloop, built 1763; *Swift*, ship-sloop, built 1777; *Swift*, cutter, purchased in 1763.

can be procured. The *Swift* has also the headrails which were more common on larger craft at this time. Her bowsprit has more stive, but this may have been changed when she was rerigged. Her bow is very much cut away on the rabbit, but the deadwood on her cutwater extends her forefoot forward.

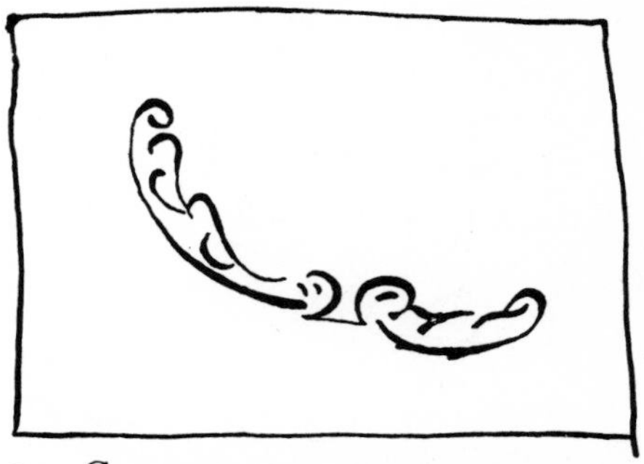

The date of this vessel's drawing, 1783, places her as being a late Revolutionary War type. She was captured during 1779 and was taken into service and refitted in 1783. The original draught gives her spar dimensions, and from this her sail plan was drawn. The spar dimensions are given here with diameters in feet and inches.

3 — CARVING ON THE QUARTERS OF THE SCHOONER "SWIFT"

DIMENSIONS

	MASTS		YARDS	
	Length	Diam.	Length	Diam.
Mainmast	47′ 6″	14″	35′ 2″	6¾″
Topmast	24′ 1″	7″	25′ 11″	4⅞″
Gallantmast	19′ 6″	4⅞″	19′ 0″	4″
Foremast	40′ 3″	13¾″	37′ 7″	7″
Topmast	26′ 0″	7⅜″	27′ 3″	5¾″
Gallantmast	18′ 1″	5⅛″	19′ 6″	4⅜″
Main boom	42′ 6″	9⅜″		
Gaff			22′ 6″	6⅛″
Bowsprit	31′ 2″	13⅞″		
Jibboom	20′ 0″	6¼″		
Spritsail yard			27′ 3″	5¾″

These dimensions are for her brig rig, as fitted for service in the Royal Navy. Her original rig was perhaps larger. It was usual to cut down the spars of American vessels when taken into the Royal Navy, as they were "overhatted" for European waters.

It will be noted that the vertical guards on the bulwark, noted on the "Virginia-built Privateer," are shown on this vessel, but they are only two in number, whereas the last named vessel had five, all aft along the quarter-deck. The *Swift* had one set forward as well as one set aft. These were more common in small war vessels of the period than in merchant craft and probably were to protect the vessel in boarding.

The deck layout of the *Swift* is a good example of early American Clipper schooner and brig practice. Beginning at the stern she has a tiller on deck

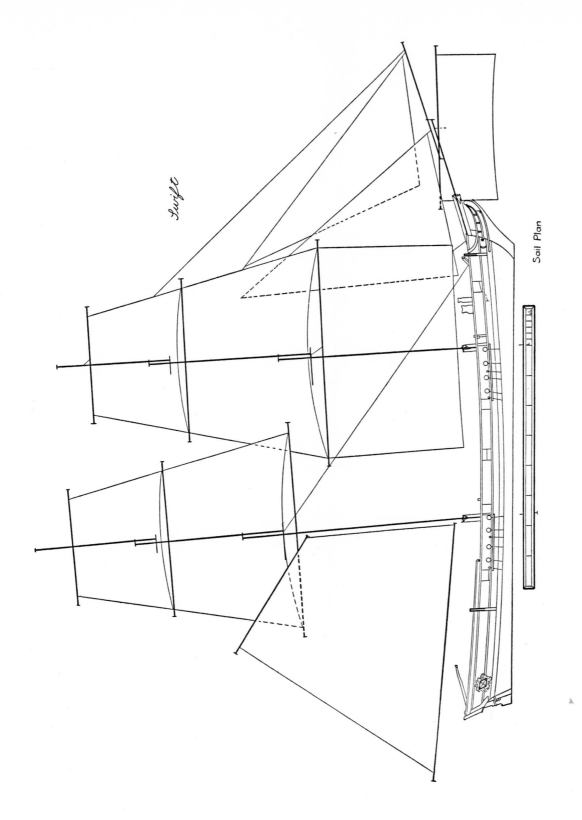

Swift

Sail Plan

A Draught of His Majesty's Sloop "Swift" as taken off

Length on deck .... 75'-6"
Keel for Tonnage .... 62'-4"
Breadth Extreme .... 20'-10"
         Moulded .... 20'-5"
Depth in Hold .... 7'-9"
Burthen in Tons 143 88/94

His Majesty's Sloop "Swift" as taken off and fitted for foreign service at the stern of the Double Dock, Deptford Yard, 3rd December, 1783. Taken from the Americans

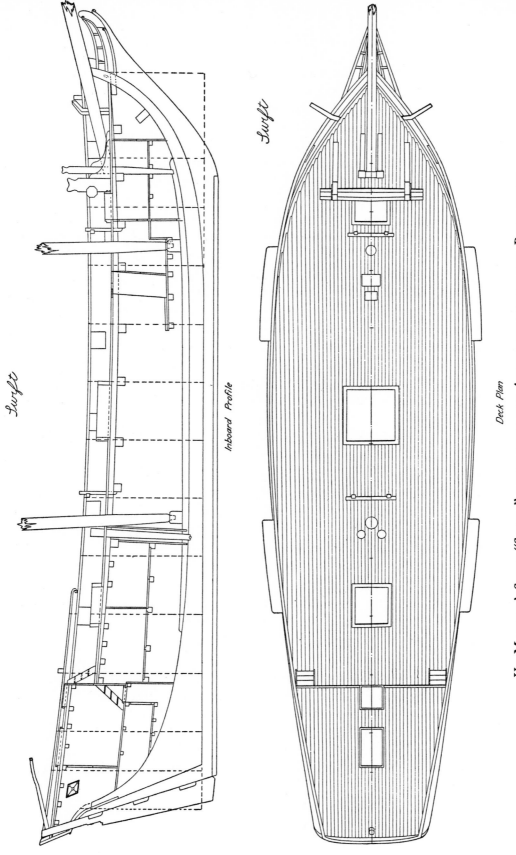

Swift

Inboard Profile

Swift

Deck Plan

His Majesty's Sloop "Swift", taken from the Americans during the Revolution

and room for one in the cabin aft; her after cabin bulkhead has a very high opening in it, that would allow a tiller to swing, and to give access to the run as well. Apparently she had no cabin or state room in her run, and the stern and quarter windows opened into the run and not into the cabin.

Forward of the tiller is a cabin skylight, and at the break of her short, raised, quarter-deck is the cabin companionway hatch. In this, facing forward, was the opening to the cabin leading down three steps. On each side, probably, were steps leading from the main deck to the quarter-deck as shown in the plan. The latter are not shown in the original draught, but as they were customary with this arrangement of deck they have been shown in the plate.

Forward of the break in the deck is another large hatch, probably opening into the officer's quarters, and forward of this are the two pump wells and the mainmast. Between the main- and foremast is the large main cargo hatch, opening into the main hold and just aft of the foremast, apparently, was the galley hatch, as a fireplace is indicated, but the chimney is not shown. This was probably of iron and could be removed. The fireplace was open at the after side, as the hearth is indicated, which undoubtedly was of brick. Just forward of the main- and foremast were light bitts, and forward of the foremast was the forecastle hatch. The forecastle was very small and there was a storeroom below it. Probably the large crews swung their hammocks in the main hold as well as in the forecastle.

There is an old-fashioned handspike windlass right forward of the hatch, with either one or two barrels, and supported by two large knees. Between these knees is a small bowsprit-bitts, supported by two smaller knees. These bitts extend to the keelson. She had catheads forward and a hawse hole through the bows, in the usual manner.

The vessel is pierced with six ports on a side, with rather low bulwarks. The bulwarks around the quarter-deck are very low, and there appears to have been no rail. This differs from the European practice, where an open rail was generally used along the raised quarter-deck.

Apparently there was no raised forecastle deck in any of these boats. The Baltimore Clipper, and the "Virginia-built" vessels do not seem to have used this type of deck arrangement. There is a construction plan in the English Admiralty, of a man-of-war schooner of 1804, the *Arrow*, which does show this, but the *Arrow* was designed and built in England, to replace a ship-sloop of the same name which had been captured. This schooner, the *Arrow*, was about ninety-one feet on deck, but apparently is not on the American model. No lines have been found for this vessel, so her sections are not available.

Returning to our example, the *Swift*, it is apparent that this is a highly developed class of ship, with very good lines and moderate power. Both the *Swift* and the "Virginia-built Privateer" show the same easy bilge, cutaway bow, raking stern post, great deadrise and large beam of the later Baltimore Clippers and the fact that these vessels are so distinct a type, during this period, tends to prove that the Baltimore Clipper, as a class of vessels, existed for sometime before the Revolution.

These vessels represent the larger class. As to the smaller vessels, there is little information to be had. Knowles shows plans, taken from Steel, of a "Virginia-built" pilot boat. If the privateer, shown in Steel, is of the Revolutionary War period, it is highly probable that this pilot schooner is of about the same date. As has been stated, Steel's book came out in 1805 and was no doubt the work of years. As it was but about twenty years between the end of the Revolution and the appearance of this book, it is highly possible that most of his work was done just after the war. If such is the case, this pilot vessel gives an idea of the small clipper schooners of this date. Her lines differ from the larger vessels in having less draft and deadrise, but the main features are unchanged. This is probably a Cape Henry pilot schooner, and like all of her class, of later years, was quite shoal.

The deck plan of this vessel is quite different from the ordinary, in that there is a sunken quarter-deck, or cockpit, in the stern. This vessel also has the transom as did the "Virginia-built privateer" and also the *Swift*. She was probably rigged as a fore and after, with a single headsail, foresail, mainsail, and maintopsail or maintopmast staysail. This, at least, is the rig of thirty years later.

The pilot boats were considered very fast, but this particular class was not the "pilot boat-built" type of later years. The later pilot boats were of the type that finally evolved into that known as the New York pilot schooner and descended from the usual Baltimore Clipper, of more draft, than the example shown.

To review our examples of the type preceding the Baltimore Clipper, we have found that the "Virginia-built" vessels are strongly noticed before the end of the Revolution. Their appearance is not different from the vessels of later years; their characteristics are the same, and the use to which the vessel was put, is that to which we referred to in the earlier chapter. We have studied their lines and deck arrangements and with this pictorial evidence before us, it is of interest to compare this class with European schooners used during the same war.

A curious example of a schooner is found in the *Carleton*. This schooner, and a slightly larger one, the *Maria*, were in the fleet opposed to General

Arnold on Lake Champlain, in 1776. This action is of no particular interest to us, technically, but the vessels engaged on the English side were largely designed and built in England, and then taken apart and rebuilt on Lake Champlain.

The *Carleton* is the smaller of the two schooners, draughts of which have been found. This vessel was fifty-nine feet two inches on deck, while the other, the *Maria*, was sixty-six feet on deck. The *Carleton* is shown here as an example of the small schooners employed by the Royal Navy and the Customs on the American coast, during the Revolution. They were comparatively shoal draught vessels, the *Carleton* carrying twelve guns and the *Maria*, fourteen. The shape of the *Maria* is very similar to the *Carleton*, except that the *Maria* has a head and cutwater with a figurehead, the full-length figure of a woman, with the usual head rails and knees. The *Maria* had oar ports between the gun-ports, whereas the *Carleton* did not. The profile of the *Maria* is otherwise the same as that of the *Carleton*. The sections of the *Maria* are very slightly different below the load waterline, but above, they have tumble-home of about a foot, whereas the *Carleton* has none.

Reference to the drawing of the *Carleton* will show European practice in schooners of about 1776. The original draught of the *Carleton* was so dated, and is titled thus: "A Draught of the Carleton rebuilt at St. Johns on Lake Champlain 1776." The open quarter-deck rails, previously mentioned, are to be seen in this drawing. The raised quarter-deck is very high for so short a vessel; there is about five feet six inches under the beams of the quarter-deck. The two vertical guards again appear on this vessel as well as in the *Swift*, but the deck is much more simple in arrangement. There is a large hatch under the fourth port from the stern and another between the fifth and sixth port from the stern. This last hatch is smaller and is either a companionway or a galley hatch. The vessel has a long quarter-deck and her mainmast is at the break. Her foremast is right in her eyes. The bowsprit evidently was at the side of the stem, so as to pass alongside the foremast, there being but about four feet between this spar and the inside of the stemport. The bowsprit had great stive, as will be noticed. She probably had a cabin aft.

Her stern is not shown, but she probably did not have a lower transom but was planked to a cross seam, as was the practice in larger ships. The profile of her stern does not indicate a square tuck and full transom though many craft of the period had this build. This vessel was of the same type as Arnold's flagship and may have been rigged the same, that is, she carried no square sails. The *Maria*, being larger, may have had the square sails. If the drawing of Arnold's flagship, the *Royal Savage*, in Volume I of Maclay's

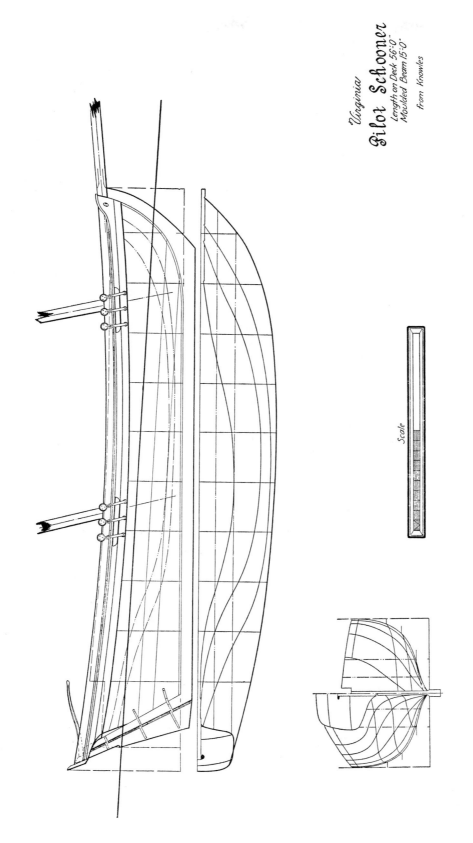

Virginia
Pilot Schooner
Length on Deck 56'-0"
Moulded Beam 15'-0"

From Knowles

Scale

"History of the Navy," is authentic, there was certainly little difference between this vessel and the *Carleton* (in profile).

This vessel has been illustrated here not only because of her historical interest but because she represents one of the few, rare, schooner plans of this early date now in existence. A comparison of this craft with the "Virginia-built Privateer" and pilot boat, the *Swift*, and similar craft, shows the very wide difference in design between American and European types. A further comparison may be made by referring to Chapman's book, Plate XL, which shows privateer schooners on the best European practice of this period. None of these European vessels shows the elements of design to be seen in the American craft, as will be discovered by a little research.

The whole question of design of the American craft appears to have been approached at entirely a different angle from that used abroad. The Americans, if they used the Bermuda or Jamaica type for a model, progressed rapidly in refining the lines and fairing the underbody until they had a model of exceptional beauty underwater. The topsides were often designed on European standards, no doubt, as in *Swift*, but only in large and important vessels. Later, this practice ceased, as the builders became bolder and more certain of their own excellence. All this, purely technical though it is, will enable the student of ship-building to correct the erroneous views gained from old pictures of American vessels of this date. It is certainly true that there were a multitude of slow, box-like tubs, but the smaller fighting craft were fine-lined schooners or brigs, cutters or sloops, and were capable of speed and able to weather out the severest weather to which they might be exposed. This is particularly true of American-built craft, since the necessity for possessing fast vessels existed throughout the American Colonial period.

The rigs have been mentioned from time to time, and from what data is available it follows that during the later days of the Revolution the schooner was the popular rig. At the beginning of this war, however, sloops and brigs were the most numerous privateer rigs. The double-topsail schooner, with a square topsail on her main, as well as one on her foremast, was a very common rig. As this rig combined the advantages of the fore and aft schooner with many of those of the justly popular brig, it resulted that a large number of privateer schooners and men-of-war carried this sea-going rig. The advantages were many, but of chief interest to the fighting sailors was the ability to stop and to back, advantages which were lacking in the fore and aft schooner, and partly lacking in the topsail schooner. This was the real reason why schooners were not as numerous as men-of-war, and why the brig was always favored, in small craft.

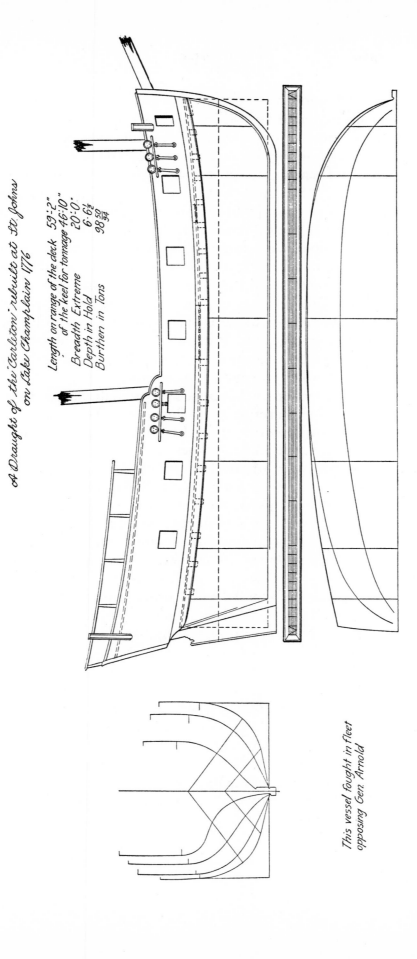

A Draught of the 'Carleton' rebuilt at St. Johns
on Lake Champlain 1776

Length on range of the deck   59'-2"
    of the keel for tonnage   46-10"
Breadth Extreme   20-0'
Depth in Hold   6-6¾
Burthen in Tons   98 59/94

This vessel fought in fleet
opposing Gen. Arnold

The European designer of schooners, however, desired first of all a shoal-draught gun carrier. Speed and sailing qualities were of minor importance, but handiness and capacity were first considerations. Some, as Chapman, for instance, designed a number of fast schooners, but the type was not popular either with the French or English during this period. The French preferred the lugger, and the English the cutter class. This European type of schooner-rigged gunboat, as that was really what she was, is clearly expressed in the design of the *Carleton* and *Maria*.

The European schooner did not progress until after the Revolution and during the French wars after 1790. This was due to the fact that the French acquired many schooners from the Americans and employed them largely in the West Indies. To combat these, for obvious reasons, it was absolutely necessary to build vessels of the same specifications and the English began to build a superior fast schooner. When the American schooners purchased by the French either wore out or were lost, the French, too, began to build their own. The Dutch also copied the Americans.

The American schooner of this period has been discussed from the technical standpoint wholly. In returning to the historical side, it will be possible to indicate the constant growth of the "Virginia-built" vessel, or the Baltimore Clipper type, into the leading American class of vessel.

After the first two years of the Revolution had passed, England began to campaign in earnest. She had a navy comprised of about 228 vessels, of which 55 were rated as sloops. At the end of the war, in 1783, she had 555 vessels of which 217 were rated as sloops and 43 as cutters. Some of these two classes were really schooners as well as cutters and brigs. Opposed to this increasing navy, were a number of converted merchant ships, a few captured or purchased men-of-war, a small number of fine American-built frigates, and a number of small fishing craft — pilot boats, coasters and West India traders. From the West Indian traders and the pilot boats there came a few suitable vessels for privateering. The pilot boats were largely schooners or sloops, and the traders, schooners or brigs. As soon as possible, these were fitted out as privateers, or government vessels.

Built for fast sailing they proved fairly successful against the great odds which they had to face. The other classes soon disappeared for their lack of speed was their destruction. It did not take the enterprising colonial sailor long to come to this conclusion and he soon began to build fast vessels, from the best available model, the "Virginia-built" vessel, or, in other words, those built around the Chesapeake Bay districts.

Due to the lack of records there is no exact list of "Virginia-built" craft engaged in privateering during the war, but it would not be erroneous to

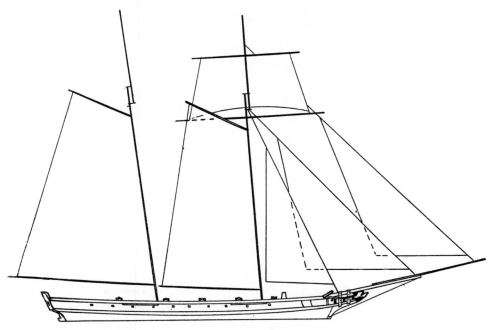

TOPSAIL SCHOONER RIG PREVIOUS TO 1800

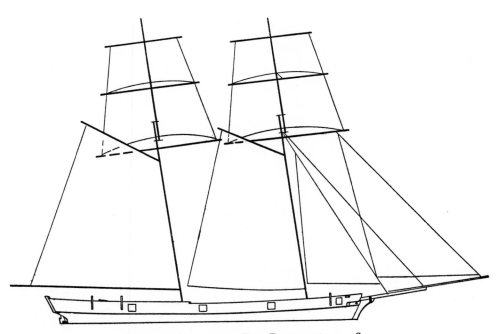

TOPSAIL SCHOONER RIG PREVIOUS TO 1800

state that fifty per cent of the American vessels engaged in this business after 1778, were "Virginia-built" type or model.

The first mention of a successful American privateer schooner that appears in Colonial records is the *Dolphin* of eight swivels. This vessel made a successful cruise in 1776, during the fall of the year. This must have been a very small vessel. While there is an occasional schooner mentioned before this date, they are either State or Government craft. The constant mention of *swivels* in early Colonial records, is curious. This type of armament is a forerunner of the later carronade. Just how these swivels were mounted in American craft is difficult to discover, but in Chapman we find a cut of this arm as used in European privateers. The accompanying sketch is taken from this work.

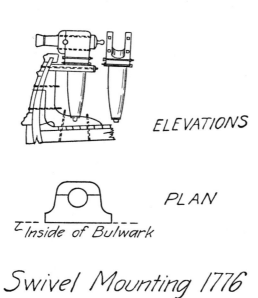

ELEVATIONS

PLAN

Inside of Bulwark

Swivel Mounting 1776

FIGURE 3

When the Americans finally resorted to open warfare, they became very active in fitting out craft for privateers. Every possible class of vessel, from ships to whaleboats, was hastily fitted out and armed with a wide variety of armament and even the weakest often made valuable prizes. During the first two years of the war, the New England Colonies, New Hampshire, Massachusetts, Rhode Island, and Connecticut, sent out 89 privateers, New York sent out 7, New Jersey 1, Pennsylvania 13, Maryland 21, South Carolina 6, and North Carolina 3, a total of 142 vessels. Massachusetts with 53 and Maryland with 21 were the two leading Maritime Colonies, and the large number of vessels from the Southern Colonies indicates the great activities of the builders on the Chesapeake.

Massachusetts had a large number of schooner privateers during this period, but whether or not they were of the Virginia model it is now impossible to state. It is highly probable that the vessels from the southern colonies were of the Virginia model even as early as this.

The trend of privateering during this war can be shown by the number of vessels engaged: 136 to 142 vessels in 1775-76, 73 vessels in 1777, 115 vessels in 1778, 167 vessels in 1779, 228 vessels in 1780, 449 vessels in 1781, and 323 vessels in 1782. The variation in number, from year to year, indicates the fortunes of war on land and the state of the blockade as well, for the blockade was badly disrupted when the French entered the war in 1778, which was followed by a decided gain in the number of private armed vessels. This not only indicates the encouragement that French aid gave to the colonists but shows the more material advantage, the opening of more ports, for the appearance of the French fleet on the American coast lifted the blockade on the southern coast and released a large number of privateers, particularly in the Chesapeake.

Fincham, the English naval constructor, in his "History of Naval Architecture," * tells of the changes that took place in the British Navy during the war. Apparently the state of the navy was greatly improved with the entrance of France into the war, with particular reference to the design of new ships. The state and interest of the Royal Navy during the life of the "Virginia-built" vessels and the Baltimore Clipper will be of continued interest, as this navy, more than any other, was in constant contact with this type of vessel, and through capture and purchase acquired a number of them for naval service. It is from this condition that we are indebted for some of the plans of schooners and brigs that are available.

The increase in number of vessels engaged in privateering and the improvement in the vessels of the Royal Navy, opposing these privateers, would have a tendency to improve the class of vessels built for privateering service. It would be a natural and inescapable result that privateers would improve in speed and increase in size and gun power. Since the Provincial Navy declined steadily in number of ships, the privateers had to assume many of the duties of regular naval ships, and because of this came nearer, with the passing years of war, to the high state of perfection of regular naval craft, in gun power, speed, and seaworthiness.

It would be useless, for our purpose, to describe the various actions of the Revolution. They add very little to our knowledge of the ships themselves, as even the descriptions are often erroneous and of no help to the technician. The handling of the vessels in action, the seamanship, in other words, comes under a different study than the one we are engaged in. The points that have been touched upon in historical references are merely those which have direct bearing on the work in hand.

By the end of the war the vessels that had been engaged in privateering had become a distinct type. The various phases of their development during the Revolution have become vague through the mists of time. The names of their builders or designers and owners are lost, except for a very rare reference.

* "History of Naval Architecture," London, 1851.

We can speculate, however, upon the spread of the so-called "Virginia-built" models, during this war. It is apparent, both from the name applied to the type and the history of privateering during the war, that the type was first introduced in Virginia and the Chesapeake Bay. Due to the vigorous prosecution of the naval war, the type became popular and spread along the coast. It must be kept in mind that, during the life of the Baltimore type, its whole existence was centered in the necessity for speed. Had not the Revolution brought out the need for seagoing fast vessels, heavily armed, the type would have remained a very small class, comprised of small pilot boats and traders. As it happened the demand for this type, so able to fulfill the privateering and naval needs of a young and struggling nation, became so great that the type became national. It is quite possible that had it not been for this war, the American vessels would not have been of this type, or at least, the type would not have developed so quickly. The rapidity of the improvement of this class of vessel, considering the well-known conservatism of the times and particularly of ship-builders and sailors, is amazing. From the type represented by the Bermuda sloop and its probable modifications, these vessels soon developed into the *Swift* and the "Virginia-built Privateer," and other similar models.

In closing this period it is interesting to note the absolute necessity of the quality of speed, above all others, in American vessels. Probably no other maritime nation was so weak in national vessels as were the Colonies, and so their merchantmen had to depend on their heels for existence. This, while very trying on the nerves of the early seamen, was a splendid development in the history of American ship-building. Soon this very speed, so necessary in running, was applied to chasing, with very good results, as is seen in the list of prizes.

At the end of this period, then, we find that the Baltimore Clipper type, as exemplified in the "Virginia-built Privateer," was well known and popular. They were large and heavily armed and sparred. They became noticed and casual references in the pages of naval histories begin to appear. Their speed and success had begun to attract the attention of ship designers abroad, and we find schooners mentioned very often in English, French, and Dutch naval histories. The American vessels sold abroad, mainly to France, had advertised the type, and their popularity was assured. From the end of the war our field of research opens up and more data becomes available.

CHAPTER III

DEVELOPMENT FROM 1782 TO 1812

WHEN the Revolution was over the Americans had vessels built for speed only, very sharp on the bottom, with very little hold or cargo space as a result. Fitted to carry guns only it was impossible to crowd enough cargo into their narrow holds to make them pay as freight carriers, and so these vessels were sold to French and Spanish interests, largely in the West Indies, for privateering and naval service. These countries, engaged in a naval war against England, soon put them to work, with disastrous results to Britain's commerce in the Caribbean Sea.

The *Atlante*, mentioned in the last chapter, is an example of this class, and it may be of interest to describe in detail her capture in an action with an English packet ship.

On December 1, 1793, the King's packet ship *Antelope* was off Cumberland Harbor, Cuba, having cleared from Jamaica three days before, bound for England. Here she discovered two French schooner privateers of heavy force lying in wait. As soon as the packet's commander discovered these vessels, he made all sail for Jamaica and aid. The two schooners made chase and one of them, the *Atlante*, outsailed her consort and continued the chase alone. The packet more than held her own until the afternoon of the following day, when the wind dropped and the *Atlante*, resorting to her sweeps, soon came up alongside. After an exchange of shots, the privateer sheered off, but an hour later swept up and grappled the packet on the starboard side. The *Atlante*, in the usual privateering method, poured in a broadside and attempted to board under cover of the smoke and confusion occasioned by her fire. The crew and passengers of the packet, however, succeeded in driving the privateersmen back with heavy loss.

The commander of the packet, Captain Curtis, the steward, and a passenger, were killed in the first broadside. The first mate was also wounded severely and the command was taken over by the acting second mate, Pasco, the boatswain.

The packet's crew and passengers under the command of this officer, engaged in hand-to-hand fighting of desperate character until at last the privateersmen, having had enough, attempted to sheer off. Mr. Pasco, noticing that the grapplings were being cut, ran aloft and lashed the schooner's square sail yard to the *Antelope's* fore shrouds. The packet then poured a heavy volley of small arm fire into the schooner and she at once surrendered.

James, in his Naval History, states that the *Antelope* mounted six 3-pounders and sailed with 27 men in her crew, of which four were lost by fever and two more were ill in their hammocks. Her total loss in the action was three killed and four wounded.

The *Atlante* mounted eight 3-pounders and had a crew of 65 men composed of French, Americans, and Irish. Her losses were the first and second captains and 30 men killed, and 17 officers and men wounded. The *Antelope* safely brought her prize into Annotta Bay, Jamaica, on the morning of the 3rd. It is to be added that the packet had a number of French emigrants, ex-officers, largely, who fought bravely against the republican privateersmen.

While the Americans did little privateering during the war with France, this war produced the schooner *Enterprise* of the United States Navy. In 1799 the Secretary of the Navy wrote to the Navy Agent at Baltimore, that the regular ships of the navy were too slow to cope with fast-sailing privateers and directed him to have built two fast-sailing schooners for this service. These two schooners were built and named *Enterprise* and *Experiment*. They mounted twelve 6-pounders. The first commanding officer of the *Enterprise* thought she was too lightly built, and that her quarters, in particular, should be bullet proof. In 1800 her armament was increased by two more 6-pounders and she was rated as fourteen guns. Her dimensions are given with some variation at different periods, due to the different methods in measuring. Capt. Stephen C. Rowan, writing in the "Rhode Island Mariner," concerning this craft, gives the following lists of dimensions, as of the year 1816:

Length along the deck	83 ft. 6 in.
Length of the keel	60 ft.
Beam	22 ft. 6 in.
Depth of hold	11 ft. 6 in.
Tonnage	165

In an old "Running Ledger," covering a period of years, her dimensions are given as:

Length between perpendiculars	84 ft. 7 in.
Length of the keel	71 ft. 6 in.
Moulded beam	22 ft. 6 in.
Overall beam	24 ft. 6 in.

Draft forward	9 ft.
Draft aft	13 ft. 6 in.
Height amidships of portsill	3 ft. 5 in.
Tonnage	228

These measurements are after she was converted into a brig. Captain Rowan states that there is reference to her having been lengthened at Venice, in 1805, but that there is no official order for this.

In 1803 the Secretary of the Navy ordered the Navy Agent at Baltimore to have two more schooners built, of the following dimensions:

Length on the gun deck	84 ft.
Length of the keel (for tonnage)	60 ft.
Beam, moulded	22½ ft.
Beam, extreme	23 ft.
Depth of hold	9½ ft.

Later, a letter stated that these were the dimensions of the *Enterprise*.

William Price of Baltimore built one of these schooners, said to be exactly like the *Enterprise*, which was launched as the *Vixen*. Instead of building the second schooner, the *Nautilus* was purchased.

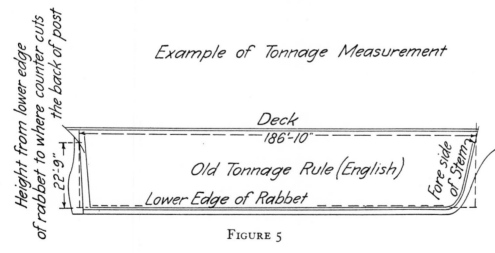

FIGURE 5

Now arises an interesting question, into which the entry of the *Nautilus* brings out a few points of interest. It is highly probable that the *Enterprise* and her sister vessels were not of the extreme type. The Royal Navy schooner *Sea Lark*, very nearly meets the dimensions of the *Enterprise*. The *Sea Lark's* measurements, as given in the draught, are as follows:

Length of the main deck	81 ft. 3 in.
Length of the keel for tonnage	65 ft. 2⅞ in.
Breadth, extreme	22 ft. 8 in.

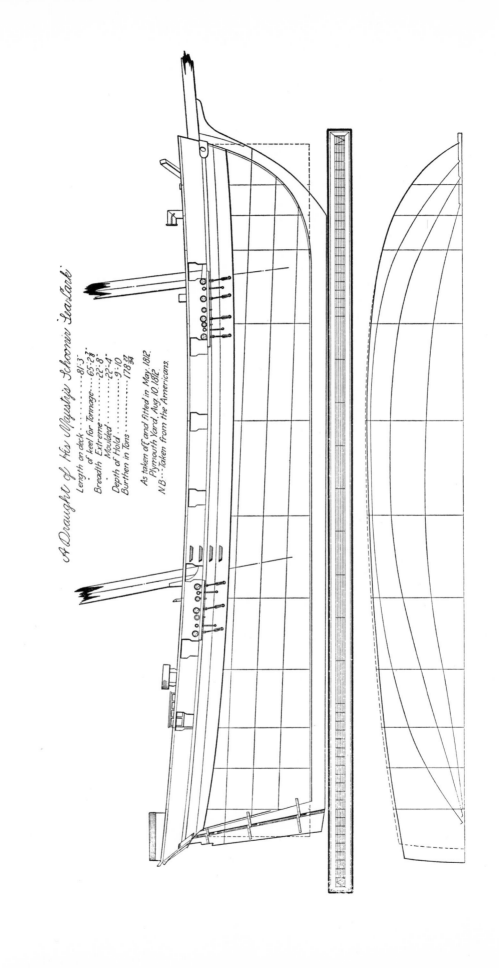

A Draught of His Majesty's Schooner Sea Lark.

Length on deck - - - - - - - - 81'·3"
  · of keel for Tonnage - - - - 65'·2⅞"
Breadth Extreme - - - - - - - - 22'·8"
  · Moulded - - - - - - - - 22'·4"
Depth of Hold - - - - - - - - 9'·10"
Burthen in Tons - - - - - - - 178 27/94

As taken off and fitted in May 1812.
Plymouth Yard, Aug 10 1812.
N·B—Taken from the Americans.

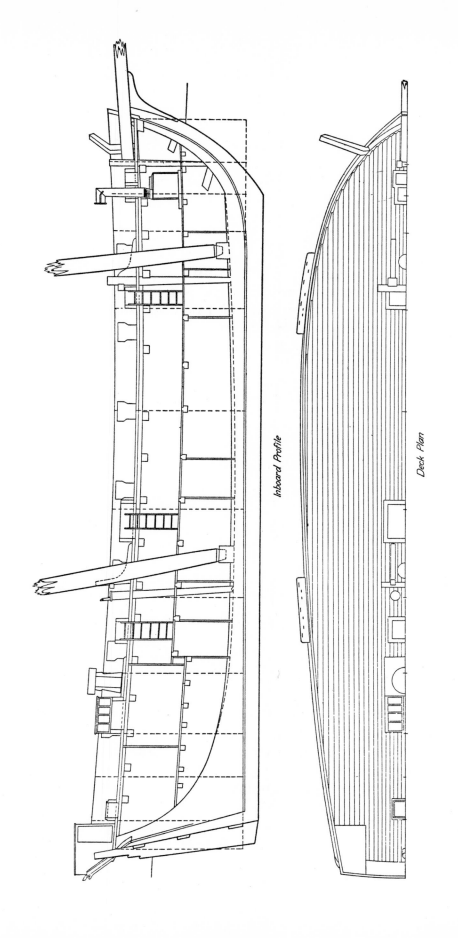

Inboard Profile

Deck Plan

Breadth, moulded   22 ft. 4 in.
Depth in hold   9 ft. 10 in.
Burthen in tons (English measurement) 178 27/94

On the original draught there is a pencil notation of a proposed schooner of the same lines with the following dimensions:

Length on deck   80 ft.
Breadth, extreme   23 ft. 6 in.
Breadth, moulded   22 ft. 8 in.
Depth of hold   10 ft. 6 in.
Burthen in tons, say   180 tons (English measurement)

Reference to this vessel will show that she would carry twelve guns, and that she was pierced for fourteen. Her rake and stern post is not great, as compared with the usual American practice. This point will be referred to again. Her rig is given and her spar dimensions were as follows:

SEA LARK
DIMENSIONS OF MASTS AND SPARS

| | MASTS | | | YARDS | | |
| | Length | | Diam. | Length | | Diam. |
	yds.	in.	in.	yds.	in.	in.
Main, hounded	24	23				
Reduced in 1817 to	21	22	18⅝			
Head	2	2				
Top, hounded	8	0	6⅞			
Pole	2	0				
Fore, hounded	22	16				
Reduced in 1817 to	19	18	19⅝	17	7	9
Head	2	12				
Top, hounded	7	14	8¾	10	19	6¾
Pole	3	26				
Bowsprit	8	8	17½			
Jibboom	8	17	7⅝			
Main boom	17	31	11⅝			
Main gaff	8	17	6¼			
Fore gaff	8	6	5¾			
Topgallant yard				6	25	4

The accompanying sketch shows this rig in place. For so small a craft she carried an extremely large rig. The Royal Navy cut her down in 1817, for European service. This particular vessel was in active service in the Royal Navy for some years and was a popular vessel.

The different methods of finding the length of keel is due to the method of tonnage measurements. The length of the keel of the *Sea Lark*, along the straight at the bottom, is actually about 69 feet. The *Sea Lark* was taken from the Americans during the summer of 1812 (there is a pencil notation on the original draught to this effect). The title of the original draught is "*Sea Lark*, Schooner as taken off, and fitted in May 1812, dated 10th of August 1812. Received at the Admiralty Aug. 12th, 1812." This means that her lines, taken off in August, are as she was fitted out as an American in May, 1812.

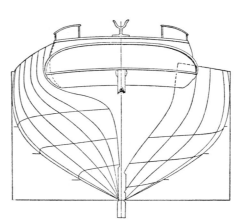

The *Vixen*, rigged as a brig, and the *Nautilus* were both captured during this war, but the *Sea Lark* cannot be either of these vessels as the *Nautilus* became the *Emulous* after her capture, and no plans are now to be found. Since the *Vixen* became a brig, this plan of the *Sea Lark* does not represent her, but it is of a very similar vessel, without doubt. In the Royal Navy she carried ten 12-pounders, carronades, and probably a carriage long gun,

FIG. 6 — LINES OF THE SCHOONER "SEA LARK"

as in many of the American privateers. It is a great pity that the past history of this vessel is not available but further research may bring it to light eventually. There are no plans of the *Vixen* in the Royal Navy Collection that have been found and it is possible that her name was changed after capture.

The other American schooner of this size was the *Viper*, rated as ten guns in the United States Navy, but she is said to have been captured in 1813; the *Nautilus* was captured in 1814. Certainly, if these dates are correct, the *Sea Lark* cannot be either of them as she was in English possession by August, 1812. The plans of the *Sea Lark*, however, are introduced to be compared with the point brought up by the purchase of *Nautilus*.

When the *Nautilus* was about to be bought through the Navy Agent, Captain Bainbridge recommended against it, because she was so sharp forward that she could not stow more than five months' provisions, and because her rake of stem was so excessive that she could not bear the weight of the guns in her bow ports (for chasers), and also because the rake of her stern post, being equally great, prevented her from carrying stern chasers of the desired size. This indicates that the *Enterprise* and *Experiment* were much less extreme than the *Nautilus*. The last vessel was probably of the type represented by *Flying Fish*, or *Grecian*, while the *Enterprise* and her sisters, more nearly approached the *Sea Lark* in model.

The naval officers did not particularly like the Baltimore schooners, and the extreme models not at all, as they would not stand up under a load of heavy guns. These schooners were built for speed only, and privateers did not carry heavy guns in great number, but large crews. They did not fight artillery battles, but, after firing a broadside, or their long gun, if small, they closed and tried to board. The naval vessels could not be handled in this manner and as the Baltimore type was not suited for naval methods, it was only natural that Captain Bainbridge should not approve of the *Nautilus*. Naval vessels, of small size, were expected to be able to fight an artillery battle when, with consorts, they attacked a larger vessel, or when fighting a vessel of their own class in regular battle.

Apparently then, the *Enterprise* class had less rake in the ends than did the usual Baltimore schooner of her date. The *Enterprise* with the *Experiment*, *Vixen* and *Nautilus*, represent the type of naval schooner before the War of 1812. Engaged in the suppression of piracy in the Mediterranean, in privateering in the West Indies, and in coast guard work, they had active and successful careers up to the time of the war.

It is in connection with the *Experiment* of twelve guns that we came across a reference to three-masted schooners. In 1800 she was chased in the West Indies, by two French privateers, one of which was a three-masted schooner privateer of fourteen guns and sixty men. The captain of the *Experiment* hove up, when darkness came on, and let one of the privateers pass him in the dark. Having separated the two vessels, he proceeded to attack the three-master, which struck, after a short action. Her name was "*la Diane*."

The three-masted rig seems to have sprung into being about 1790, and became rather popular in the West Indies. This was due to a number of causes, but chiefly to the desire for more sail on a vessel of given size. Reference to the rules of masting for three-masted schooners will show how the increase was made. The rig was applied to both French and English schooners, but does not seem to have become popular with the Americans.

After the American Revolution there was a reduction in displacement of the Baltimore Clippers, for they no longer carried as many guns. This was done by decreasing the draft, and usually the beam, slightly. This class of vessels was engaged in the West Indian trade and the pilot service. The general model was like that of the earlier Cape Henry pilot schooners, shown in the Knowles or Steel plate. However, this type, with a little more depth and with large rigs, proved very fast and became popular in the West Indies. The French and Spanish procured some of them, along with many of the former Revolutionary privateers.

Many of this shoal class of schooners were rather crank, due to their

TOPSAIL SCHOONER "FAME," OF SALEM, 62 TONS, BUILT AT
IPSWICH IN 1795

From a water color painted in 1800 by William Ward, in the Peabody Museum, Salem

UNITED STATES JACKASS-BRIG "PICKERING," OF NEWBURYPORT
187 TONS, BUILT AT BOSTON IN 1798. LOST AT SEA

Probably near Guadeloupe, in the gale of September, 1800

Reproduced from a mezzotint in the "Naval Chronicle," Vol. 33 (1815)

A VIRGINIA PILOT BOAT GETTING UNDERWAY.

Published by T. McLean, 26, Haymarket.

From a lithograph drawn by J. Rogers in 1825, in the Macpherson Collection

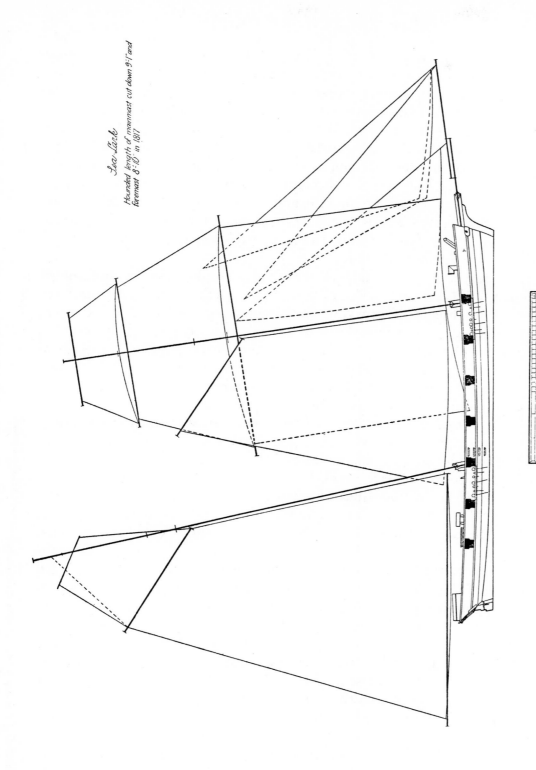

Sea-Lark

Hounded length of mainmast cut down 9'1" and
foremast 8'10" in 1817

Sail Plan of His Majesty's Schooner "Sea Lark"

weight of spars and heavy masting. These two-masters were often converted into three-masted schooners, by reducing the diameter of the masts and the mainsail, and adding a driver mast. By doing this they retained the same area of sail as they had before with the two-masted rig, but escaped the weight of the long main boom. While the idea behind this change appears to have been to increase the stability as well as the speed, it was not long before a three-masted schooner had taller masts than any two-master of the same size. The rig, however, had become popular with many, due, perhaps, to the fact that it was easier to handle, and accordingly many craft were laid down as three-masted vessels. Some of these were purchased by England as well as France, for light cruisers, and by private parties for privateering, as well as more nefarious business.

Fortunately there is available a beautiful example of a later three-masted schooner. This vessel built at Baltimore sometime during the last ten years of the eighteenth century, was apparently captured from the French, and after she was taken into the Royal Navy as a 10-gun schooner-sloop, her name was changed to *Flying Fish*, a name that was popular in the Royal Navy for fast vessels for many years. After a few years of service this vessel was sent to England and her lines were taken off. From these lines a number of similar schooners were built in Bermuda.

A *Flying Fish*, while commanded by J. Prevost, was on the scene at the surrender of Cape Nichola Mole, in 1794. This was not the same vessel as the three-master, but was an earlier and smaller schooner which was captured by the French and later retaken.

Our *Flying Fish* had her lines taken off in September, 1806, at the Portsmouth Yard in England. Her draught is shown in the accompanying plate as well as the changes made in it to build the *Shamrock* class at Bermuda. During the same year, probably earlier than September, the *Flying Fish* captured several privateers at Batabano in the Isle of Cuba, while commanded by Capt. J. G. Gooding. The vessel had the reputation of being very fast, and was apparently one of that class that sailors love — "a lucky ship."

The sail plan of the *Flying Fish* and the *Shamrock* class is here reconstructed by Fincham's rule, and is approximately the rig carried during her life. Some schooners of this type may have carried square topsails on the mainmast, as well, but as the *Shamrock* class was rather tender and very wet, it is highly improbable that they carried such a rig. The *Shamrock* class was in existence from 1807-8 to about 1820, and vessels built on these lines were known in the Royal Navy as "Bermudians." They were usually 10-gun "sloops," carrying 18-pounder carronades and a crew of 50 men. The "Bermudians" were very fast, but due to their heavy armament and

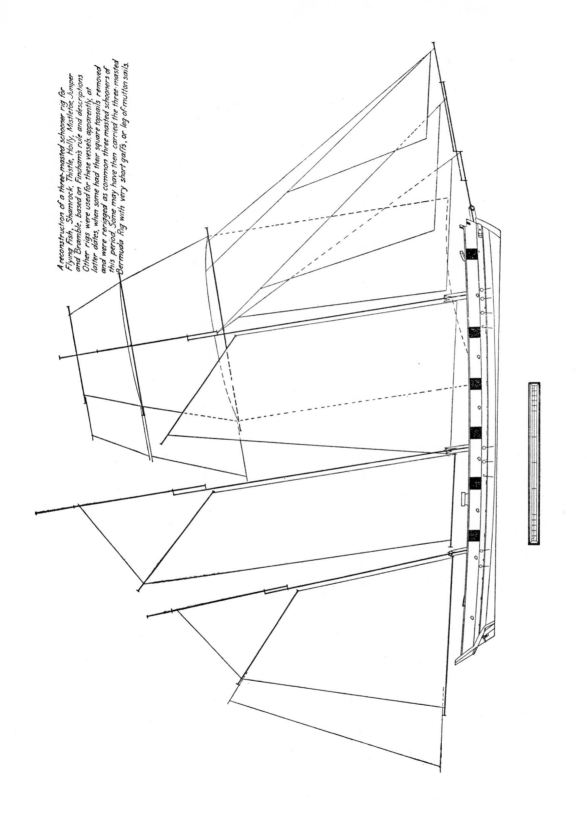

A reconstruction of a three-masted schooner rig for Flying Fish, Shamrock, Thistle, Holly, Mistletoe, Juniper and Bramble, based on Fincham's rule and descriptions. Other rigs were used for these vessels, apparently, at latter dates, when some had their square topsails removed and were rerigged as common three masted schooners of this period. Some may have then carried the three-masted Bermuda Rig with very short gaffs, or leg-of-mutton sails.

Shamrock, Thistle, Mistletoe, Holly, Juniper and Bramble built in Bermuda by Adm order of Mar 1807, as shown in profile

Shamrock Class Profile

Note:- Topsides from deck up were added to her original build

A Draught of His Majesty's Schooner Flying Fish, built at Baltimore and taken off in Sept. 1806 Portsmouth Yard

Dimensions of Flying Fish
Length on Deck ..... 78'-8"
Length of Keel for tonnage 60'-8⅝"
Breadth Extreme ... 21'-7"
Breadth Moulded ... 21'-3¾"
Depth in Hold ... 7'-10"
Burthen in tons 150 31/94

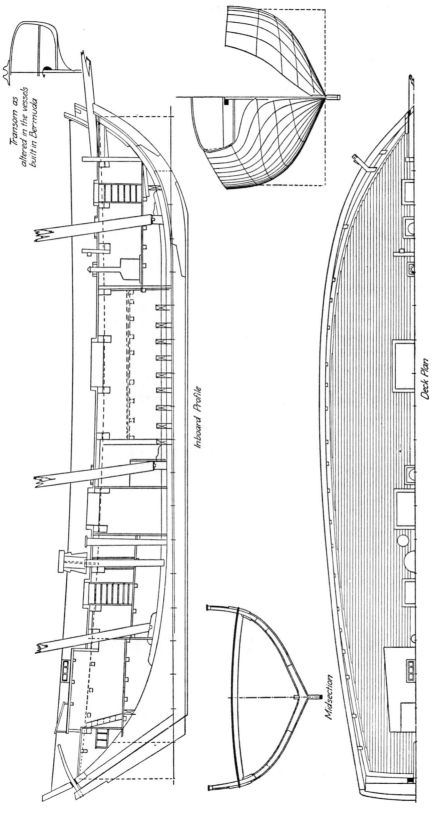

Transom as altered in the vessels built in Bermuda

Inboard Profile

Midsection

Deck Plan

INBOARD PROFILE AND DECK PLAN OF HIS MAJESTY'S SCHOONER "FLYING FISH"

Built at Baltimore and taken off in September, 1806

long masting were very wet. This heavy weight and light displacement, along with their low freeboard, made them slice through a wave without rising, and as a result they were too hard on the crews for northern stations.

The *Flying Fish*, the original model for this class, was 78 feet 8 inches on deck, 60 feet 8⅛ inches on the keel, for tonnage, 21 feet 7 inches extreme beam, 21 feet 3¾ inches moulded beam, 7 feet 10 inches depth in hold and measured 150 32/94 tons burthen. The draught represents a craft that, except for the bulwarks and stern, might be a model for a modern cruising yacht. The shape of the bow and her long, easy lines are far ahead of these of the gun-brigs of 1800-1820 and cannot but make us proud of the American builders who, at this early date, could turn out so splendid a model — a vessel whose lines were far ahead of her time. The cutaway forefoot is very marked, and the stern post's rake is greater than the vessels mentioned in the preceding chapters. The waterlines are sharper and the deadrise is slightly increased, but the bilges are very slack, and the topsides have outward flare. There are no channels, apparently. When the *Flying Fish* was taken into service, her bulwarks were raised, as noted on the original draught. Probably her original rail came up a foot or eighteen inches above her deck, or she may have had an open rail as many privateers had at that time. Her sparing and the placing of her masts, is typical of the earlier, three-masted schooners. The driver was rather close to the mainmast, which made the mainsail, a boomed sail, quite narrow and taunt, as is apparent in the sail plan. The foresail would be the same as it would be in a two-masted schooner, but a little narrower at the foot.

It is probable that the example of a three-masted schooner quoted by Fincham in his "Masting and Rigging," is one of the "Bermudians." The dimensions that are given indicate it, as well as diligent research in the Admiralty Collection. Aside from the *Flying Fish* and the "Bermudians," there was but one vessel built by the Royal Navy as a three-masted schooner and that was a packet larger and of altogether different form and also built much later.

No doubt the rig of these vessels changed a little with the passing years, but the rules for sparring three-masted schooners, as given by Fincham, supply the official rig. It seems so certain that the example of Fincham is one of this class, that the spar and sail plan has been reconstructed from this data.

There is a possibility that the *Flying Fish* was responsible for the large number of three-masted schooners built in the Bermudas between 1810 and 1840. A painting in the Macpherson Collection shows a three-masted "Bermudian" schooner entering port. Her hull should be compared with the

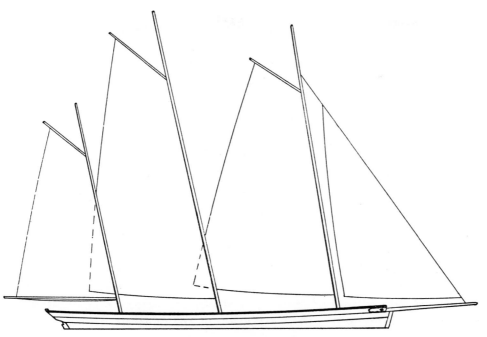

3 Masted Gaff Sail
Bermuda Schooner

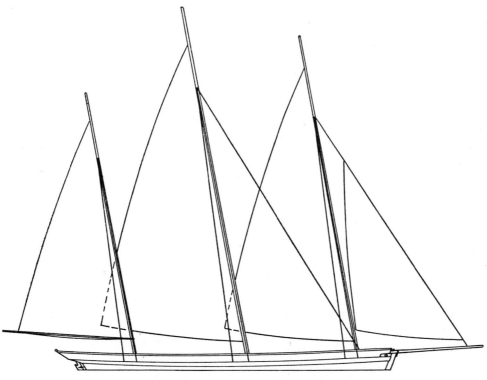

Leg of Mutton Sail Schooner
Bermuda 1820-50

Shamrock class, as there is a great deal of likeness. Her rig is three leg-of-muttons and she carries very long masts. The *Shamrock* class, ordered built in 1807 and completed during 1810-11, were built at Bermuda. These craft, in spite of their being wet, were extremely fast, and it is natural that the Bermudians would copy the model, with slight variations in hull and rig. Without guns aboard the model would not be wet and would probably be much faster and stiffer under canvas. It is probable, therefore, that here we have the parent of the Bermudian three-masted schooners, which, it will be well to add, were very well known for their speed during the 1830's.

It will be noticed by the draught of the *Flying Fish*, that her actual freeboard was very low but that her bulwarks are quite high. These bulwarks were rather lightly built, however, and probably did not injure the vessel's sailing to any appreciable extent. The ports for her sweeps are between the gun-ports, and were covered with a swinging cover, pivoted on a bolt through her bulwarks. Her gun-ports were arched. American vessels had gun-ports of varying shape before 1812. Apparently they were experimenting a little. The vessel had little sheer and her bowsprit did not have much stive. When the Royal Navy built the *Shamrock* class, the stive was the only change made forward. This was increased, as will be noticed in the draught.

The stern of the *Flying Fish* is of great interest and research in the Admiralty Collection of small war vessels and has thus far failed to bring forth anything like it. The stern post is *outside* the transom at the rudder head, which locates the rudder about eight inches aft of the transom. The vessel steered with a tiller and there is a square opening through the transom to allow the tiller to enter inboard. She has a square stern, with full transom and the transom is very high above the deck. The rudder is rather narrow, so the vessel must have steered easily.

The inboard profile of the *Flying Fish* shows the general arrangement below decks and requires but little explanation. She had a cabin house aft with the usual companionway hatch and skylight. Here were the main cabin, the captain's, no doubt. In the run was a storeroom and forward of the driver mast was another cabin, for the officers, apparently. There was a storeroom or magazine beneath both cabins. The capstan pintle was paneled in, where it passed through the cabin, and the pumps passed through a storage space. There was a large cargo space forward of this and a magazine was located at the heel of the mainmast. Amidships was taken up with a main hold, decked in to make quarters for the crew. This deck was in sections and could be removed at will. Forward of this was a galley, with a fireplace and metal smokestack through the deck. The forecastle was in the bows, with storage space below. The spacing of the floors, size and shape of the keelson, and fore and aft deadwoods, are plainly shown, as is the system of stepping the masts.

The deck arrangement is as follows: Beginning at the stern there is an open deck at the tiller with no hatches. Then comes the cabin house with the driver mast just forward of it; then the hatch leading to the officers' quarters, forward of which is the capstan and the two pump wells. Next comes the large storage hatch and the mainmast, and between the main- and foremast is the main hatch and galley stack with a small set of bitts just aft of the foremast. Between the foremast and the bow is the forecastle hatch and a bitt at the heel of the bowsprit. Her decks appear very wide and clear

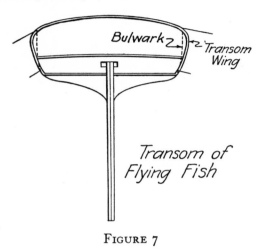

FIGURE 7

and give plenty of room for handling the large spread of canvas carried.

The changes made in this design to build the *Shamrock* class were very few. The stive of the bowsprit was increased, the top of the bulwark cut down an inch or two and a simple moulding replaced the compound rail cap of the *Flying Fish*. The gun-ports became square at the top instead of arched. At the stern, however, the transom was changed and carried abaft the rudder post, giving a rather long, overhanging transom. The carrying of the bulwark back in a fair curve changed the shape of the transom itself and gave a more graceful stern. The lower part of the transom was curved a little but no changes in rake were made nor were the positions of the masts moved. The transom, in both designs, extended outboard of the bulwarks at the wings. In the *Flying Fish* and in the *Shamrock*, the bulwark became perpendicular just forward of the transom, from the top of the bulwark at the transom to the level of the moulding above the rudder post. The shape of the transom when compared with the next section forward of it will show this.

With this example of American schooner building before us we are able to observe an extreme type, descending more from the pilot boat than from the "Virginia-built Privateer" or from the *Swift*. Because of the excellence of the model and the odd rig, she is probably of greater interest than any yet found.

The only other reference found, to a three-masted schooner during the period of the American war with France, is that of the United States brig

Norfolk losing her topmasts while chasing a three-masted schooner of large size out of Basse Terre, West Indies, in 1799. By the time of the War of 1812, however, three-masted schooners were common and the Royal Navy

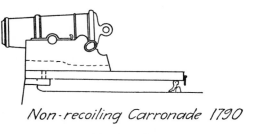

Non-recoiling Carronade 1790

FIGURE 8

had re-rigged a few in this manner. The bulwarks were light in these vessels but due to their height and windage, as well as weight, they were sometimes a hindrance to speed and it was customary, when hard pressed, to saw away the bulwarks and even the supporting stanchions, after heaving overboard the lee guns. French and English schooners of this period, built on a clipper model, are reported to have capsized through this practice by suffering a change of wind or by luffing. During the War of 1812, a number of American schooners capsized either through accidents of this kind or when overpressed with sail.

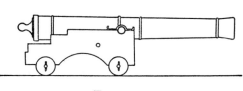

Carriage mount - Long Gun

FIGURE 9

The guns used on the Baltimore Clippers and the earlier "Virginia-built" vessels, throughout this period, differed but little from those of the Revolution, other than a gradual increase in weight of metal thrown. The most marked change was the introduction of carronades which came into use about 1790. This arm gradually replaced the swivel and because of its greater power became a very popular weapon on small naval craft. Ranging from 12 to 68 pounds, they were very destructive at close range. The 18-pounder seems to have been the most popular of the carronades in the Royal Navy, between 1800 and 1812, but the Americans preferred the long 6- and 9-pounder carriage guns. The long gun was to become the favorite ship gun by 1812 and it fitted in very well with the Baltimore Clipper design as it was comparatively light, easily handled, and accurate at long range.

Some of these guns were mounted on a pivot, but there does not seem to have been many American vessels so armed, fiction and history to the contrary. It was more efficient for a lightly armed privateer schooner to have a long gun, better known as "Long Tom," on a broadside carriage, and to shift it where needed, than to have the pivot gun, with the limited training area available on a sailing vessel. The pivot gun was used mainly on gun-boats and on a few 1-gun privateer schooners. The larger vessels seldom used it.

The pivot gun would have to be mounted above the bulwarks in some manner and none of the privateers of the larger class seem to have had any method of doing this. Their bulwarks were too high and there were no raised quarter- or forecastle decks to bring the gun up to this level, as had the privateers shown in Chapman's book on Naval Architecture, which were armed with long pivot guns. Furthermore, such a mounting offered no protection to the gunners against small arm fire at close quarters, and considering that the privateersmen fitted out with this type of fighting in view it is highly probable that this gun-mounting was not used very often in larger vessels. In very small vessels the pivot gun may have been used, with more success, as there were no real bulwarks anyway, and the carriage gun, should one be used, could not be shifted about the deck enough to be of any advantage. The small war vessels, illustrated in "Souvenirs de Marine" by Admiral Paris, which are of the period of 1790-1810, show the various gun mountings popular on European ships and, except as noted, these mountings were probably used on American schooners.

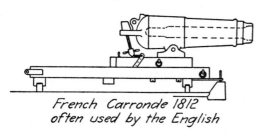

French Carronde 1812 often used by the English

FIGURE 10

Some of the carronades were mounted on broadside carriages while some were mounted on pivoted carriages, but unlike the pivot long gun the pivot was at the muzzle end of the carriage and was usually swung on the waterway or on the port sill. Other types were used on various ships but each navy generally used some standard mounting for this gun. Carronades mounted on a non-recoil carriage were ordered fitted to all rates in the Royal Navy in 1804, but the type was not popular and did not last. This mounting did not allow the guns to recoil more than the elasticity of the breaching would permit.

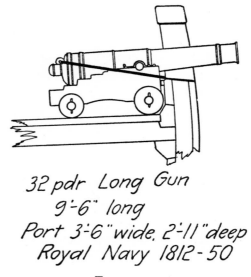

32 pdr Long Gun
9'-6" long
Port 3'-6" wide, 2'-11" deep
Royal Navy 1812-50

FIGURE 11

Due to the fact that we can find a few plans of American-built vessels in the Admiralty Collection, the observation of this period is not complete without some study of the Royal Navy from 1790 to 1812. The schooner in the United States Navy has been referred to and it is interesting to observe the changes in the British Navy at the same time. During the last decade of the eighteenth century, England was almost continually engaged in

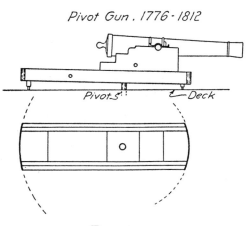

Pivot Gun. 1776-1812

FIGURE 12

war. The constant fighting with the French, forced the Royal Navy to meet a superior class of ships possessed by the French Navy, and eventually compelled its designers to copy them. This was true in all rates, from the cutter and tender to the 120-gun ships. In the smaller classes the English used mainly the gun brig and a few cutters, but the gun brig was most numerous. These vessels were matched against schooners and brigs, often on American lines, possessed by the French and also the Spanish navies.

The faults of the gun brig, in matter of speed and sailing qualities, were so obvious that the Admiralty at once took steps to improve the design of this class as well as that of frigates. A study of French, Spanish, and American models was made, both from captured vessels and those purchased, as well as experimental vessels. To this investigation we owe the plans of the *Flying Fish*. Other vessels were built, as experiments, which were similar to the Baltimore model. These vessels, rigged as brigs, were quite numerous and some of them were quite fast. The Surveyor who directed many of these experiments was Sir Henry Peake and his plans retained many of the elements of design contained in the fast American schooner of this period. Some of his vessels were too narrow and had to be hipped out, but the majority were very fast vessels of their date and type.

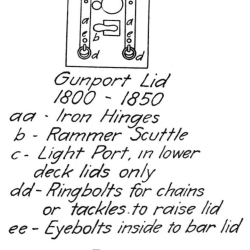

Gunport Lid
1800 – 1850
aa - Iron Hinges
b - Rammer Scuttle
c - Light Port, in lower
  deck lids only
dd - Ringbolts for chains
  or tackles to raise lid
ee - Eyebolts inside to bar lid

FIGURE 13

Of this class of vessels, the Americans took a few in 1812-15, including the *Epervier*, designed in May, 1812, by William Rule and Henry Peake; the *Frolic*, built in the *Rolla* class, probably (the *Rolla* was designed in 1807

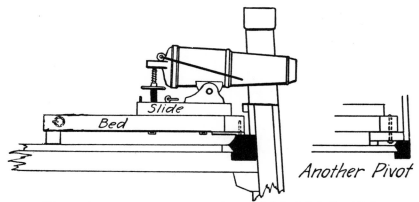

Slide

Bed

Another Pivot

Recoiling Carronade R.N. 1808-1820

Slide held to Bed by two bolts
moving in slot in Bed.

Bore 4.6" – 12 pdr. (muzzle to back of base ring) 2'-9"
" 5.2" – 18 pdr   "   3'-6"
" 5.7" – 24 pdr   "   3'-8"

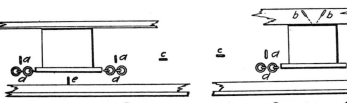

Carronade Port   Long Carriage Gun Port
(Inboard View.)

e - Pivot Pin in waterway   bb - Eyebolts to lash muzzle
of gun to in bad weather.

a·a Train Tackles Eyebolts
c·c Extreme Train Eyebolts

d·d - Breeching or preventer Eyebolts, outer one
for emergency

Royal Navy 1812 - 1840

and had the heel of the stern post cut off, giving the same effect as a rocker keel); and the *Boxer* (when captured this vessel was described by her American captors as a "fine, fast sailing brig"), which was of the *Contest* class and designed in 1811.

This last class was very active against privateers on the American coast, and was fairly successful. The *Manly, Bold, Borer, Snap, Swinger* and *Plumper* were all of this class and were on the American station throughout the war. Their mid-section, except for being of greater area, is similar to the American Baltimore type.

The *Avon, Peacock, Penquin* and *Pelican*, all of them brigs which took an active part in the War of 1812, were of the *Bacchus* class. The *Bacchus* was a brigantine sloop and it is probable that the others were the same. The mid-section of this class was rather similar to *Flying Fish*. These were designed in 1811 by Henry Peake.

During 1796 to 1798 a number of experimental schooners were built after designs by Bentham. While no plans exist, from existing descriptions it appears they were of similar lines to a whale boat, from 80 feet 6 inches to 86 feet 6 inches long, on deck, with a sharp canoe stern and a mid-section that was rather round on the bottom with a strong flare out at the sides. The vessels were of peculiar build and their transverse strength depended on diagonally planked bulkheads. They had deep, false keels and some deadwood fore and aft to hold them in windward going. These vessels were very fast and seaworthy but for some reason they were not repeated. One or two were fitted with "sliding keels" (centerboards).

A large number of schooners were purchased at this time but no plans exist so nothing is now known of their form. It is probable that they were built in the West Indies, and occasionally an American vessel was bought or seized and taken into service.

For this class Bermuda furnished quite a number. In the years 1802 to 1808 a number of Royal Navy vessels were built in Bermuda. Many of them were built as sloops or cutters and later converted into schooners. Incidentally it is curious to note that vessels in the Royal Navy rated as cutters, particularly in the 4- and 6-gun class, were, in reality schooners, and a large number of them were built in Bermuda in 1804; the *Lady Hammond* class, for example; and again, in 1805, the *Haddock* class. These were very small vessels and were built to carry 10- to 18-pounder carronades in the 1804 class, and 6- to 12-pounder carronades in the 1805 class, but because of their lack of displacement they had difficulty in carrying their rating. The size of the guns varied in each of these vessels and some carried more or less guns than originally fitted for.

The *Lady Hammond* class was built on the lines of a very fast Bermuda sloop and twelve were constructed. They were very lightly built and quite extreme, having a rockered keel and raking ends. They were 68 feet 2 inches on deck by 20 feet 4 inches extreme beam, and their depth in hold was 10 feet 3 inches and burthen 110 74/94 tons. Originally rigged as sloops or cutters, a few were changed to schooners. Though fast they were not liked as they could not carry guns enough to make them of use as cruisers, and due to their light displacement, cut-away underbody, and heavy sparring, they were very ticklish craft when under a press of sail in strong breezes. Like the "Bermudians" they required very careful handling to keep them from going "lost." Many were lost through foundering and as a class they were not long lived.

The 1805 or *Haddock* class is of particular interest in that this class was so unfortunate as to furnish the first and last national vessels captured by American privateers in the War of 1812. The *Whiting*, captured in August, 1812, by the *Dash* privateer and returned to the English, due to irregularity in her capture, and the *Landrail*, captured by the *Syren* in July, 1814, were of this class.

James, in his Naval History, states that these vessels carried four 12-pounder carronades and 20 men. They were 56 feet 2 inches on deck, 18 feet 3 inches extreme beam, 8 feet 9 inches depth in hold, and 75 tons burthen. Fifteen were built in Bermuda, of pencil cedar, between 1804 and 1807, and twelve were built in England on the same lines. These vessels were somewhat like the Baltimore Clippers in model but due to their small size were rather tubby and their speed was not as great as the *Lady Hammond* class. The *Haddock* class had sections very like the *Sea Lark*, and her profile was somewhat similar except that she had no head and was, of course, much smaller.

The experiments in this class were carried out rather haphazardly in an effort to procure a class of small cruisers. Unfortunately the faults of the Admiralty ideas of design were very apparent and spoiled all these classes as naval vessels. The principal fault was in making the dimensions of these craft far too small for their gun rating with the result that they were all very much overloaded. This fault was not limited to the lower rates but extended to ships-of-the-line and it was a long time before it was finally corrected and the various rates became really large enough to properly carry their guns and stores.

The attempts to improve the small cruisers in the Royal Navy, while not bearing directly on American clipper models, had the effect, in the long run, of improving the Baltimore type. The Baltimore vessels, after having been sold to England's foes, were forced to meet and sail against these improved types and so necessarily keep step with the improvements in fast sailing craft, even though the United States had little interest in the wars with England. When the 4- and 6-gun cutters were being built in Bermuda it is said they were observed by Americans and that these men thought the Baltimore schooners would have been superior as cruisers. However, the Royal Navy agents considered the smaller vessels they were having built better able to fill the needs of the service, which certainly was not proved by later events.

The whole period between 1790 and 1812, in all navies, seems to have been distinctly a period of improvement. How much of this was due to American schooners is now mere speculation, but certainly they had much influence in laying out the lines of the small rates and special cruisers of the English and French navies. The English schooners, in particular, showed the effects of the American model, as much as the English frigates showed the influence of French practice. The majority of the frigates built during this period were built on the lines of captured French vessels of this rate, and the United States frigates that were built in these years showed both French and English practice, as well as a number of distinctly American ideas.

After 1800 the schooners of the clipper model were being built in Europe on lines that were more or less exact copies of the Baltimore model. The English, French, Spanish, and Dutch schooners show the American influence for fifty years after 1800. Brigs were also built that showed the same influence but they were fewer in number. By 1812 the Americans were considered the leading builders of schooners and their vessels the acme of this rig. Their employment in the West Indies has been mentioned and their introduction as vessels of war was followed by their being used as merchant craft. Very soon the West Indian builders were making copies with modifications to fit their needs. Some of these copies were equally extreme in build when compared with the Baltimore Clipper.

A favorite class of schooner was called the "Ballahou." This was a sharp-floored, fast-sailing schooner with fore-and-aft sails of great hoist and no topsails, the mainmast raking sharply aft and the foremast nearly vertical. This rig was popular from about 1806 on. It is mentioned in the War of 1812 and existed for many years after in the West Indies and Bermuda. It is possible that the present schooner rig, popular at Barbadoes, is an offspring of this rig. This type of masting was also called the "Bermuda Schooner rig," at a later date.

It is during the period under observation that the "pilot boat model" became popular. This model of the Baltimore Clipper was the standard type for privateers, during the War of 1812. The model was a direct offspring of the "Virginia-built Privateer" type, which has been described. It differed

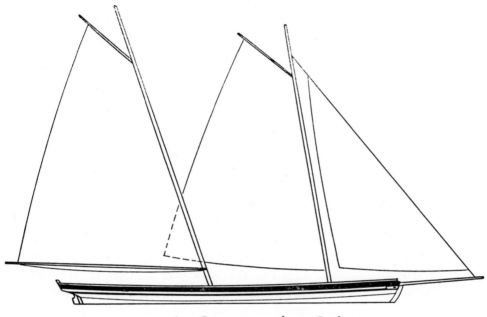

2 masted Bermuda Schooner or Ballahou Rig.

FIGURE 14

from the Virginia pilot boat, as shown in Knowles' and Steel's plate, and from vessels of the *Flying Fish* class, in having greater proportionate beam and deadrise with the result of increased draft. This increased sharpness of the floor gave a better windward boat, and having a greater amount of ballast lower down enabled it to carry a greater press of sail in strong winds. Apparently these vessels did not carry a greater spread of canvas, as a rule, than the shallower type, as all rules for rigging were based on beam and waterline length; but the deeper class was certainly more able. The causes that brought out this model are beyond our ken, but it was probably due to the growth of the ports of Philadelphia, New York, Boston, and Salem. These ports, becoming larger, and having an increasing tonnage, brought about greater competition among the pilots, so that they went further offshore than before and had to have larger and more able schooners. Except for the Virginia Capes, the schooners could carry a greater draught of water and so instead of building the Virginia type pilot boat schooner, the deeper model, as illustrated in the privateer models, became used in building pilot boats.

Beginning with the Baltimore privateer model the builders of New York and Boston increased the deadrise and draught until they evolved the type that was popular for many years, the New York and Boston pilot schooners. The distinguishing mark of this class of vessel seems to have been the lack of a head. The knee of the head, trail boards, or figureheads do not seem ever to have been very popular with the pilots. Only when this class was again employed for privateering, do the heads come back, and then merely as gammon-knee heads, without any decoration, as a rule, other than occasionally a scroll or simple billet. It is highly probable that many of the privateers did not have the head at all and had bows like the *Flying Fish*, particularly the smaller schooners and of course the ex-pilot boats.

The pilot boat model became very extreme in deadrise just after the War of 1812, but during the period just previous to the war it did not differ very much from the type popular during the war for privateering. Their freeboard was always very low and this was the distinguishing mark of American schooners for many years. The rake of the stern and stern post was very great, in Baltimore practice, and the beam was large. The rig of this model was probably a regular fore-and-aft schooner, without square topsails of any kind. They may have carried a square-sail yard when fitted for long voyages and may have had square topsails, too, but this was not the regular rig.

The demand for speed in this service was always great. This demand, to which the Baltimore Clipper owed its existence, is still another reason for the development of the model. The demands of this service, as well as the sale of the American schooners for West Indian privateers and traders, all combined to bring out the best models available for the services required. Adding to this the competition and rivalry between individual builders and the large ship-building communities, we find a tremendous urge, financial and sentimental, to improve this one class of vessel. The sale of a fast sailing schooner offered no difficulty and the enterprising builders, knowing they had a market, built on speculation. As long as a builder could produce a vessel that would outsail ordinary craft, he had no cause to fear financial reverses. Following the close of the Revolution, this demand rapidly increased. The abolition of slavery in England and her Colonies, and the treaties built up around it, resulted in a widened demand for the pilot boat and Baltimore schooner. With two types available, the shoal-hulled type, as in the *Flying Fish*, and the deeper pilot model, the builder could meet the demands for nearly all conditions of water, as long as speed was paramount. It is therefore apparent that in war, privateering, pilot boat service, trade and smuggling, as well as slaving and piracy, the Baltimore Clipper, and her modifications, were very actively engaged during the period of transition.

The mention of piracy calls attention to another employment for this class of American schooners. It is not necessary to enter into individual cases; they are too numerous and have no direct bearing on the situation, other than to furnish another outlet for the building of fast-sailing schooners. The rise of piracy, with particular reference to that in the West Indies, was directly due to the state of chaos that followed the continual wars between the large European powers. After the suppression of the buccaneers, piracy was not particularly annoying to commerce, except for occasional outbursts, until the end of the American Revolution when the constant employment of privateers in the West Indies, by the contending powers, brought together a fleet of fast-sailing schooners and brigs, with a few ships, manned by adventurers, ex-convicts, naval deserters and the riffraff of the seven seas. As soon as peace was declared, they were thrown out of lawful employment, and naturally turned to piracy for a livelihood. Between wars there were numerous piratical outbreaks, particularly between 1800 and 1820.

This condition was merely another contributing factor in the development of the design of the American schooner. Most of the schooners used in piracy, during these years, were built in the United States or in the West Indies, on Baltimore models. It is probable that schooners were built for this business just as surely as they were built, in later years, for privateering and the slave trade. A vessel built for piracy would be merely a privateer model, and there were plenty of excuses for turning out a vessel of that class, during this period, even though the country of the builder was not at war.

It is remarkable that the Baltimore Clipper and the disturbed condition of the West Indies are so bound together. With the exception of the period of the Revolution and during the War of 1812, the demand for the Baltimore Clipper keeps pace with political and natural troubles in the Caribbean. Certainly trouble and unrest were the Baltimore Clipper's foster parents.

No mention has yet been made of how the type achieved its name. It is nearly impossible to trace this point, other than to give the names applied to this type during its existence. The name "Virginia-built," or "Virginia model," was used, apparently, from the time of the Revolution until after the War of 1812. During the same time the type is often referred to as the "pilot boat model." This name seems to have been applied from 1808 on as well as "Virginia model." The name "Baltimore-built" first appears during the War of 1812, and in the slave trade it became very much used. The other names, "Virginia-built," "pilot boat model," "Virginia model," etc., dropped out, and the name "Baltimore" was used to characterize the type. The most common name, "Baltimore Clipper," was popular at the time the type was dying out, in the last days of the slave trade, say 1835 to 1850.

The word "clipper" has been much discussed and it seems to be agreed that it is derived from the old phrase "to clip" or "to clip along"—to move fast. This was merely a tag name for the type and later it became the name of the splendid, fast square-riggers of the '50's. While it is impossible to place exact dates on the changes of names for this type, as they overlapped and were used together at times, nevertheless, the general periods of changes of name are apparent. The reasons for these changes in name are again merely matters of speculation and have nothing to do with the lines or models of the type in which we are interested.

The names "Virginia-built," "Baltimore-built," or "clipper," "pilot boat model," etc., show merely the popular idea of where the type was being built or where it originated and the use to which it was most commonly put. During the War of 1812, for example, the descriptions generally picture "a beautiful pilot boat model schooner," or a "beautiful pilot boat," "a long, low, pilot boat built schooner," etc. This was because of the fact that the type was commonly represented best in the offshore pilot boats and so would be best known to seamen in this service. With this digression let us return to the type itself.

The various influences that entered into the motif of design in the Baltimore Clipper have been discussed at length and references have been made to the influence of the clipper on foreign schooners, particularly the French and English. In mentioning the French schooners it was stated that they were copies, largely of the American schooners bought in after the Revolution. While this is apparently true it is worth while to know that a number of French schooners were built during this period, and while their design was perhaps based on American practice, nevertheless they differed widely from the type represented by the *Flying Fish* and *Sea Lark*.

During the last twenty years of the eighteenth century, the French built three schooners whose plans are shown in Admiral Paris' work, "Souvenirs de Marine," Vol. 5, plate 270. These were called *L'Agile*, *La Biche* and *La Decouverte*, all about 84 feet long. Their sections are extremely like those of the *Flying Fish* but somewhat slacker in the bilge. Their rake in the ends is great, particularly at the stern post. The stem is very curved and nearly perpendicular above the water. The drag of the keel is noticeable and they had rather a strong sheer. The most marked difference between these three schooners and the American schooners was in the stern. The French schooners had a sharp stern with a false transom or platform, above the planksheer, something like the stern of the old New England pinky, or the present Chesapeake bugeye with the so-called patent stern. The masts of these French schooners do not rake the same, they are two-masters, and the main rakes aft much more than the foremast does, a Ballahou rig, in other words. The vessels had a small gammon-knee head and no decorations.

These three vessels, probably built sometime between 1780 and 1800, were employed as naval cruisers. Designed and probably built by M. Ollivier, he noted that they lacked sufficient beam for the necessary stability. This seems to have been the fault with many French schooners built during this period. James mentions a schooner in the Royal Navy, the *Decouverte*, in action near San Domingo in 1808. She carried eight 12-pounder carronades, and 37 men and boys in her crew, so was apparently a small vessel. It is highly possible that this vessel is the same as the one figured in Admiral Paris' work and that she was captured by the English and taken into service. No plans of this vessel seem to exist in the Royal Navy Collection, at least, none have yet been found.

This period is deserving of a great deal of further study and research and it is hoped that much more concerning individual vessels may become available by these means, and that plans of more vessels may be discovered from whose appearance it will be possible to make further deductions as to the real influence of the American type. It is probable, too, that it will be found that the Americans, also, were influenced by the experimental work done in foreign navies. All this may eventually become available. The French and English collections of draughts, and those in Holland, will probably bring out many points of interest.

We have now passed over the period of transition and traced the changes in model, variations in rig, and appearance through this time of unrest and disturbance. Due to the demands of this period, perhaps more than to anything else, the Baltimore Clipper developed rapidly to its highest form, the notorious American privateer schooners and brigs of the War of 1812.

CHAPTER IV

THE WAR OF 1812

THIS period, into which we are now entering, saw the Baltimore Clipper at its highest degree of excellence. The changes of the preceding years were consummated in the privateer schooners and brigs that saw service during the War of 1812. The natural development of the type had reached a point, by the beginning of the war, that enabled the builders to produce a vessel unequaled for privateering service. Lightly built, fast, and seaworthy, these craft would carry a few guns and a large crew, all of which were the outstanding features of the type during the war.

At the beginning of the War of 1812 the American Navy consisted of about seventeen vessels, having in all 442 guns. The smaller rates, below the frigates, were the 18-gun ship-sloops *Wasp* and *Hornet*; the 16-gun brigs *Argus*, *Syren* and *Enterprise*; the 12-gun schooners *Nautilus* and *Vixen*; and the 10-gun schooner *Viper*. These, with a few surveying and custom-house schooners, were the most useful types in the national navy. Opposed to them was the Royal Navy with all the advantages gained from service against the French, Spanish, Dutch, and other European nations during the thirty years of conflict preceding the year 1812. This almost constant service had brought the Royal Navy, as a whole, to a highly efficient standard in discipline, ships, and guns. The faults of the service were many, of which impressment was probably the greatest weakness. This navy had become the largest in the world and during the first year of the American war launched thirteen 74's, one 40-gun frigate, five 38's, three 36-gun frigates, fifteen 18-gun brig-sloops, ten 12-gun brigs, and five other vessels of rates below that of the 36-gun frigate. This, alone, comprised more ships than the entire American navy.

The American vessels, however, were generally larger and faster vessels than the English vessels of the same rates; but this, of course, was of little importance when compared with the power of the Royal Navy. As a result, when war was declared, the Americans took to fitting out privateers as rapidly as possible. Procuring all available vessels suitable for the purpose, they armed them with any guns that could be had and sent them to sea. Of

French Privateer "Le Comtesse Emerian" attacking and capturing the Spanish Polacre "La Reine des Deux Sicile," and the English Ship "Darwey," September 12, 1810

From the painting by Antoine Roux, Sen., 1811, owned by M. Alfred Fabre

Clipper Topsail Schooner "Surprize," capturing the British ship "Star," January 27, 1815

From a water color in the Peabody Museum, Salem

PRIVATEER BRIG "GENERAL ARMSTRONG," OF NEW YORK

From a painting by Emanuel Leutze, showing the vessel attacked by a British fleet, at Fayal, September 26, 1814. Courtesy of Robert Fridenberg

particular use were the pilot schooners. These, though small, because of their sailing qualities were considered to be the most satisfactory type at hand. Usually fitted with one long gun, either a pivot or a carriage gun, a few swivels or a small carronade, they constituted the first class to get to sea. Some of them carried a carronade or two, or a few swivels, besides their long gun, but their chief dependence was in their "Long Tom" and boarders. Their crews were, of course, numerous for a small vessel and must have lived a hard life, cramped into a fifty or seventy-five foot vessel. Their personal armament consisted of muskets, sabers and cutlasses, boarding pikes and pistols.

Early in the war a fast-sailing pilot schooner was sent to Europe to warn American merchant vessels to stay in neutral ports, unless fast enough to escape the enemy cruisers. Vessels of this last description were hastily fitted out for home, to be refitted as privateers. Some, detained abroad, managed to fit out as privateers in France.

The first Royal Navy vessel captured by American privateers was the four-gun cutter-schooner *Whiting*, Lieutenant Maxcey, used as a dispatch vessel. This small warrior was taken by surprise in Hampton Roads, July 10, 1812, by the one-gun schooner *Dash* of Baltimore, Lieutenant Maxcey not having learned of the state of war existing. The seizure was considered unfair and the *Whiting* was returned to the Royal Navy and ordered to quit American waters at once. Another small schooner from Baltimore, the *Cora*, took a small British dispatch vessel, the *Bloodhound*, at about the same time the *Whiting* was seized, and this vessel was also returned.

The small schooners represented by these privateering vessels were intended for short cruises in the Gulf of St. Lawrence off Nova Scotia, and Newfoundland, or in the West Indies and along the American coast. They carried crews of from forty to sixty men and were powerful enough to capture the average merchant vessel, but not strong enough to stand off a letter-of-marque or small naval cruiser.

From Coggeshall's "History of American Privateers," we can learn a few details of the first vessels to fit out from Baltimore for privateering.

Name	Long guns	Short guns	Crew	Types of guns
Rossie	1	13	120	12s, 24s, 6s
Comet*	2	12	120	9s, 12s
Dolphin	2	10	100	9s, 12s, 6s
Nonsuch		12	100	12s
Highflyer*	1	7	100	12s, 6s
Globe	1	7	90	9s, 12s, 18s
America	2	14	115	9s, 24s, 6s

Name	Long guns	Short guns	Crew	Types of guns
Bona	1	6	80	12s, 6s
Tom*	2	14	130	12s, 18s, 9s
Sparrow*	1	5	80	12s, 6s
Revenge	2	14	140	8s, 12s, 24s
Rolla*	1	5	80	12s
Joseph & Mary	2	4	83	18s, 24s
Wasp	1	1	50	9s
Sarah Ann*	1	1	50	9s
Liberty	1	1	50	9s
Hornet*	1	1	50	9s

The *Liberty* was rated as a one-gun sloop in some reports. The others were apparently schooners. Those with crews of less than ninety men were probably pilot boats. The *Rolla*, for instance, was but 79 feet long, 20 feet 2 inches beam and 8 feet 3 inches depth of hold, roughly, the size of the *Flying Fish*. The *Rolla* was captured, became a Canadian privateer, and was lost at sea with all hands. The *Rossie, Comet, Dolphin, Tom, Revenge,* and *Highflyer* were successful vessels. The last named had a rather hectic existence. She started as a Baltimore privateer, was captured by the English and taken into service as a tender, and after an active existence in this service was finally retaken by an American frigate. The small vessels carrying one long nine-pounder and one short gun, are the so-called one-gun schooners, in type, small Cape Henry pilot vessels. Some of these small vessels were sloop rigged, perhaps.

From New York's active harbor, there were sent out during the first year of the war, in spite of a rigorous blockade, an extremely active lot of privateers. These, too, were largely pilot boats or on the pilot boat construction.

The following list gives an idea of their size, type and power.

Rig	Name	Long guns	Short guns	Crew
Pilot schooner No square sails	Teazer*	1	2	50
Schooner	Paul Jones	1	16	120
	Marengo	1	6	50
	Eagle		1	45
Schooner	Rosamond	1	12	132
Schooner	Benj. Franklyn	1	8	120
Sloop	Black Joke	1	2	60
	Rover	1	1	35
Schooner	Orders in Council*		16	120
Schooner	Saratoga		18	140
	United We Stand	1	2	50
	Divided We Fall	1	2	50

The vessels marked * were captured or lost during the war.

Rig	Name	Long guns	Short guns	Crew
Schooner	Gov. Thompkins	1	14	143
	Retaliation	1	6	100
	Spitfire	1	2	54
Sch. or brig	Gen. Armstrong*	1	18	140
Schooner	Jack's Favorite	1	4	80
	Yorktown*		18	160
	Tartar		6	80
Brig	Holkar*	2	16	160
Brig	Anaconda*		16	160
	Patriot	1	2	50
	Union		1	24
	Turn Over		1	50
Schooner	Right of Search	1		60
Schooner	Bunker Hill*	1	4	

The vessels marked * were captured or lost during the war.

The most notorious of this list of vessels was the *Teazer*, pilot boat schooner, without topsails, classed as a two-gun vessel. She also had sweeps to move her in a calm. She was finally captured and burned. The *Black Joke*, sloop, later carried five guns, instead of three and was successful early in the war. The *Orders in Council*, a large topsail-schooner privateer, was very successful, but finally captured, being chased under the guns of a 74 by three English privateers. The *General Armstrong* is one of the best known. She was destroyed at Fayal by a fleet of English men-o'-war, after a desperate resistance. This was in 1814. The *General Armstrong* was a large and powerful privateer, either a double-topsail schooner or a brig. She is referred to as having both rigs and sometimes she is said to be a brigantine. It is probable that she was a double-topsail schooner, as this rig was often used by large privateers and slavers. This vessel had a very successful career.

The topsail schooner *Saratoga* lasted throughout the war and was perhaps one of the most active and destructive. She is pictured in Coggeshall's book in a rather poor lithograph, but was apparently the usual pilot boat type with a longer head than most of them had. She won fame by taking an English letter-of-marque brig, in 1812, a vessel armed with twelve long 9-pounders and a crew of sixty men.

The *Anaconda* is described as "a beautiful vessel, she was built in Middletown, Conn., and owned in New York. She carried 16 carriage guns and 160 men." She was a brig and after a successful career was taken by a cutting-out expedition, a boat attack, while at anchor at Ocracoke Inlet, N. C.

The *Anaconda* was taken into the Royal Navy as a light cruiser, was in the New Orleans expedition, and was sold in the West Indies about 1816. She was a very fast vessel, but probably was built of green timber.

The brig *Holkar* was another successful privateer that went too often to the well. After a successful voyage she was chased ashore in Long Island Sound, near New London, by a blockading frigate. The crew escaped, after repulsing a boat attack, and the frigate destroyed the brig soon after.

The *Bunker Hill* was a schooner of 179 tons, British measurement, carried six guns and after her capture became a Canadian privateer of three guns.

The *Right of Search* is said to have been a very small pilot schooner, but little is known of her. It would be interesting to know how the *Turn Over* received her name and it is to be hoped that she did not live up to it. She was probably another of the ubiquitous pilot schooners, and like the *Teazer*.

These schooners were generally small it will be noted, but later on in the war a larger class of vessels were built and fitted out.

Another sample of the American schooners was the pilot-boat-built schooner *Washington*, 65 tons, a prize. The privateer brig *Warrior* was described as "a beautiful brig of 430 tons [Am.] burthen, built on the pilot boat construction, carried 21 guns and 150 men." H. M. schooner *St. Lawrence*, formerly the American privateer *Atlas*, was described as "a long, low pilot boat built schooner with yellow sides." She carried 15 guns and 75 men, when in the Royal Navy.

The *Governor Gerry* is referred to as follows: "Fair Haven, Mass. Oct. 23rd 1812. The beautiful new privateer *Governor Gerry* of 250 tons [Am.], pierced for 18 guns, was launched from the shipyard of this village Wed. last. She is a most beautiful vessel, built of the best materials, and good judges are of the opinion that she will be a remarkable sailer. The keel of this vessel was laid only 48 days previous to the launch."

The privateer *Reindeer*, of 22 guns, was built near Boston in 1815. She was coppered and built of the best materials in thirty-five working days. The privateers *Avon* and *Blakely*, said to have been on the same lines as the *Reindeer*, were each launched in eighteen working days.

The American privateer schooner *Harlequin* of Boston, or Portsmouth, was described by James, in his "Naval History," in referring to her capture, as follows: "The American privateer-schooner *Harlequin* of Boston, measured 323 tons [English] and mounted 10 long, 12-pounders with a crew of 115 men. Her main-mast was 84 feet and her fore yard 64 feet in length. Her bulwark was of solid timber and four inches higher and two inches thicker than that of the British 18 gun-brig sloop."

In another reference James remarks: "None can compete with the Americans in the size, beauty, swiftness, or seaworthiness of their schooners. They will arm a schooner of 200 tons with seven guns, including a traversing

18- or 24-pounder, and give her a crew of at least 100 able-bodied men."

Before referring to other privateers, it may be well to name the American national schooners employed in the war, mostly customs and surveying schooners. They were the *Ferret, Alligator, Nonsuch, Surveyor, Spark, Flambeau, Firefly, Torch,* and *Spitfire.* The *Alligator* capsized during the war, and the *Nonsuch* and *Surveyor* were captured.

The schooner *Atlas* hailing from Philadelphia, armed with thirteen guns, was taken by boats in Ocracoke Inlet, N. C., along with the *Anaconda.* They were both taken into service in the Royal Navy, and the *Atlas* was renamed *St. Lawrence.* On Feb. 26, 1815, this schooner, under the command of Lieutenant Henry Cranmer Gordon, was sighted by the American privateer-brig *Chasseur,* the "Pride of Baltimore," about 36 miles from Havana, Cuba. Here then, opens a desperate battle between two Baltimore Clippers, on nearly equal terms. The *St. Lawrence* carried 13 guns and 76 men, while the *Chasseur* had 14 guns and 102 men. The *St. Lawrence* was being used as a dispatch vessel, and the *Chasseur* was prowling in the Florida Channel looking for a victim.

On the 26th, at about 11 A.M., the *Chasseur* sighted the *St. Lawrence,* to the northeastward, running down the wind, bound for New Orleans. The *Chasseur* made all possible sail in chase and at about noon had gained enough on the schooner to make her out as "a long, low, narrow pilot-boat schooner with yellow sides," a man-o'-war. When the schooner made out the brig, she hauled up to the northward and made sail to escape, as was the duty of a dispatch runner. At about 12.30 the schooner lost her fore-topmast and the *Chasseur* fired a gun and showed her colors, to ascertain the nationality of the schooner, to which no attention was given. The schooner, after the loss of her fore-topmast, trimmed her sails and took a turn to windward. At 1 o'clock, the *Chasseur,* having gained on the schooner, due to her accident, they were close enough to see that she showed but three ports and had very few men in sight. This led Captain Boyle of the *Chasseur* to believe that she was a poorly armed running vessel, Habana bound. The schooner about this time fired a stern-gun and showed English colors. Due to the belief of the *Chasseur's* captain that the chase was poorly armed, little preparation was made to fight. At 1.26 P.M. the brig was close alongside of the *St. Lawrence,* when suddenly the schooner triced up ten gun-port covers, gave three cheers, and poured in a heavy broadside. Her decks were alive with men in the uniform of regular men-o'-war's men.

The Yankees were completely surprised but in spite of their astonishment were able to get their guns to work and returned the fire with both great guns and small arms. They either had to fight or surrender as they found themselves matched against a fast-sailing man of war, which was distinctly not to the liking of any privateer captain.

The *Chasseur*, privateer fashion, tried to close and board, but the *Chasseur*, which was coming down very fast, shot under the schooner's lee and that vessel, putting up her helm, tried to fall off across the brig's stern, to rake. Captain Boyle, seeing his danger, also fell off and the schooner, traveling fastest now, went ahead, the vessels being about thirty feet apart. The broadsides of both vessels were very destructive at this short range and the privateer, at 1.40 P.M., suddenly closed and boarded, upon which the schooner surrendered at once.

The surrender of the schooner *St. Lawrence* was due altogether to the superior gunnery of the American. The *Chasseur* was damaged mostly in the rails and rigging and had but five killed and eight wounded, while the *St. Lawrence* was damaged in both hull and spars, her masts falling after the battle. She had fifteen killed and twenty-five wounded. The *St. Lawrence* was armed with twelve short 12-pounders and one long 9-pounder, while the *Chasseur* had six 12-pounders and eight short 9-pounders, ten of her original sixteen 12-pounders having been thrown overboard when the brig was chased, just previously, by an English frigate.

The next battle between clippers that will be of interest is the *Dominica-Decatur* action. This action will be of even greater interest to us due to the fact that we have plans of the *Dominica* to study. There are a few points that are questionable and before describing the action let us consider one of the vessels.

The plan of the *Dominica* is from the original Admiralty draught. She was a clipper schooner of 203 25/94 tons burthen, 89 feet 6½ inches on deck, 71 feet 8⅝ inches length of keel for tonnage, 23 feet 1 inch extreme beam, 22 feet 9 inches moulded beam, and 9 feet 3¾ inches depth of hold. She steered with a tiller and had quarter galleries and a long head. The draught shows her to be a two-masted schooner, and the various deck plans, according to Mr. Knight, the Admiralty Curator, also show but two masts. Unfortunately all of these deck plans are not at hand, but the best one is shown in the plate. Most of the reports of the *Dominica-Decatur* fight refer to the *Dominica* as a three-masted schooner, carrying twelve short 12-pounders, two long 6-pounders, one brass 4-pounder, and a short 32-pounder on a pivot. She had a crew of 88 men. This is one of the few references to a large schooner having a pivot and as the draught shows no place for it, one cannot but help wondering where and how it was mounted. There may have been a mounting on the main hatch as this seems to be the only avail-

HERMAPHRODITE BRIG "DIOMEDE," 223 TONS, BUILT AT SALEM, MASS., IN 1809
From a water color in the Peabody Museum, Salem

AN AMERICAN SCHOONER CHASED BY H.M.S. "ANDROMANCHE"
From a water color by G. Tobin (1813), in the Macpherson Collection

AMERICAN SCHOONER ESCAPING FROM H.M. SLOOP OF WAR "PYLADES" DURING THE WAR OF 1812

From a water color by G. A. in the Macpherson Collection

DOUBLE TOPSAIL PRIVATEER SCHOONER "FRANKLIN"

From a painting in the Macpherson Collection

able place, unless the gun was fixed to fire through the forward ports which seems more likely.

This schooner was a handsome vessel and her lines were taken off June 12, 1811, at the Deptford Yard, by Robert J. Nelson. There seems to be no information as to where she was built. It is possible that she was a captured French schooner, built on American lines, or a purchased American schooner. She was not, it seems certain, English built. If the reports of her capture by the Americans are correct, she was a three-master of that time and was so rigged during her short existence as an American privateer. She differs little from the general run of privateers; her inboard profile shows her arrangement below decks and needs no explanation.

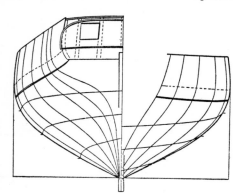

FIG. 15 — LINES OF THE SCHOONER "DOMINICA"

The *Decatur* is not so well known to us and there is very little information available other than that she was a seven-gun schooner with a square topsail on the foremast. She was two-masted, of course, built on the pilot-boat construction, and owned at Charleston, S. C. She, too, had a pivot gun, a long 18-pounder, as well as six 12-pounders, and carried a crew of 103 men. Her captain was a famous privateersman, Diron,* and his crew was well trained. She had been a very successful vessel and was finally captured June 5, 1814, by an English frigate off Mona Passage, after an eleven-hour chase. This *Decatur* was the third and last vessel of this name in the war.

On Aug. 5, 1813, when a little south of the Bermudas, the *Decatur* was heading north, under small sail, on the lookout for an English merchant vessel, as she was then in the track of the West India traders. About 10.30 A.M. the masthead lookout saw two sails, both running south. The *Decatur* spun on her heel and took a turn to the southward, to get the weather gage, so that, if the strangers proved to be too heavy, she could get away. It was the custom of the small Royal Navy cruisers to sail in pairs, due to the losses they had suffered in fighting the heavy American cruisers single-handed. By 11 o'clock the *Decatur* was close enough to make out the strangers as a ship and schooner, which, seeing the privateer, came about to meet her. The three vessels now approached one another and at 12.30 P.M., the *Decatur* being to windward, fell off, and ran to leeward, upon which the schooner

*Capt. Dominique Diron was in command of a French privateer in 1806, which was destroyed near San Domingo. James accuses him of also being quite piratical at that time.

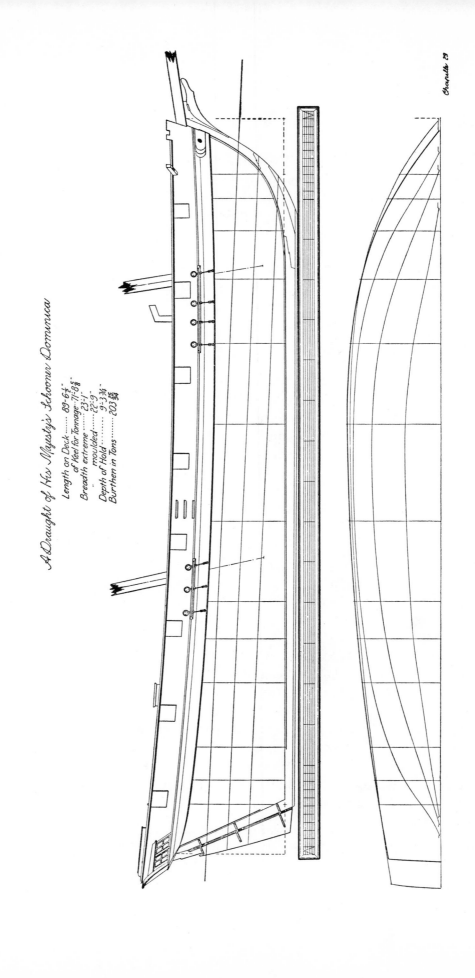

A Draught of His Majesty's Schooner Dominica

Length on Deck .... 89-6½"
.... of Keel for Tonnage ... 71-8⅝"
Breadth extreme .... 23-1"
.... " moulded .... 22-9"
Depth of Hold .... 9-3¾"
Burthen in Tons .... 203 ⁵⁵⁄₉₄

Chapelle 29

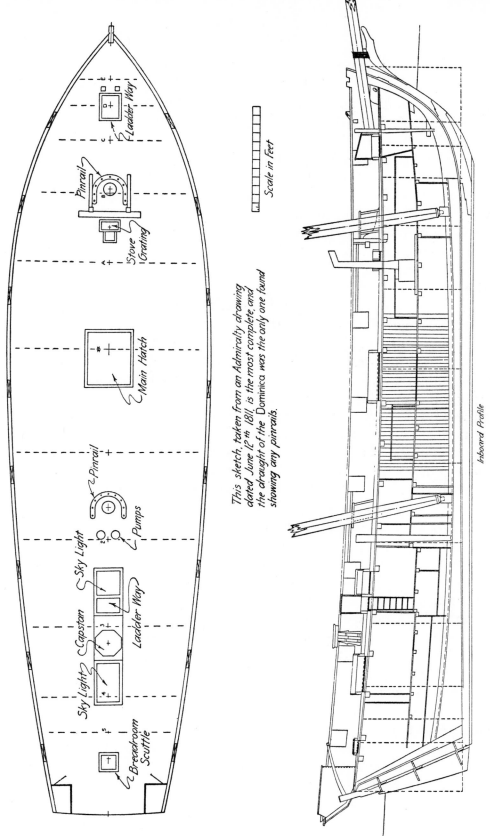

Dominica Schooner

Ladder Way

Pinrail

Stove Grating

Main Hatch

Pinrail

Pumps

Sky Light

Capstan

Sky Light

Ladder Way

Breadroom Scuttle

This sketch, taken from an Admiralty drawing dated June 12th 1811, is the most complete, and the draught of the Dominica was the only one found showing any pinrails.

Scale in Feet

Inboard Profile

INBOARD PROFILE OF HIS MAJESTY'S SCHOONER "DOMINICA"

showed English colors. Captain Diron was now aware that he had a man-of-war schooner and a packet to fight, so at about 1 o'clock he again hauled to windward. At 1.30 P.M. the schooner fired at him but the shot fell short.

Having been close enough to make out that the three-masted(?) schooner was heavily armed, Captain Diron decided that his best chance would be to close as fast as possible and board, as he knew that his crew was the largest, so he cleared for action, secured his hatches to prevent his crew from running below, and after hoisting American colors and loading his guns, ran to leeward again, to pass under the stern of the schooner, to rake. This was about 2 P.M. He planned to fire his whole broadside, close and board, but the stranger luffed and fired a broadside, which was high. Fifteen minutes later the Americans opened with their pivot, with disastrous results to the enemy, upon which the English schooner began to fire more carefully and started to open the range. In order to prevent this the *Decatur* followed in the wake of the schooner, after receiving a broadside while turning. Had this been well aimed it probably would have cost the Americans another privateer. While the broadside guns would still bear, the English schooner maintained a galling fire, but when they saw the Americans were trying to board, they filled away with the Americans dead astern. Bow to stern they sailed for a short time neither side being able to do much damage. The Americans again tried to close without success as the schooner was as fast as the *Decatur*. However, in avoiding this attack, she gave the *Decatur* another chance to close and at 3.30 P.M. the Americans ran their bowsprit over the Englishman's stern, her jibboom piercing the enemy's mainsail, and boarded, the two crews fought desperately on the crowded deck and after the English had lost very heavily they surrendered.

The Americans found they had captured H. M. schooner *Dominica*, Lieutenant Barrette, who was among those killed. The total losses in this action were *Dominica*, 18 killed and 42 wounded; *Decatur*, 5 killed and 15 wounded. The packet ship did not take any part in the battle and fled as soon as the Americans won. The *Dominica* was carried into Charleston and later fitted out as a 4-gun privateer with a crew of 36 men, but was captured again on May 23, 1814, by an English ship-of-the-line.

Evidently the vessels were both about the same size and speed. The Americans were more accurate in their fire and handled their schooner a little better. Their larger crew also gave them the advantage when they were able to board.

It is difficult to check, in the report of this action, the rig of the *Dominica*. It is stated that the *Decatur* ran her bowsprit over the *Dominica*'s stern and that her jibboom pierced the *Dominica*'s mainsail. At first glance it would appear that this inferred that the *Dominica* had but two masts, yet this could also happen if the rig in question were a three-masted schooner, as in this rig the mainmast is in about the same position as that of a two-master, while the driver or mizzenmast is quite close to the main. This may be seen by comparing the mast positions of the *Flying Fish* and the *Sea Lark*, in their sail plans. It is strange that none of the deck plans reported show the *Dominica* as a three-master, but it is possible that she was as the reports state. Coggeshall in his "History of American Privateers," does not make any statement as to this, so we have merely the newspapers and private reports to refer to.

The next action that is of interest in connection with the history of the Baltimore Clipper is the battle between H. M. cruiser *Laura* and the American privateer or letter-of-marque schooner *Diligent* of Philadelphia, ten guns, Captain Grassin. The *Laura*, also of ten guns, was commanded by Lieutenant Hunter, R.N., and belonged to the class of 4- and 6-gun sloops or cutters built in Bermuda in 1804-5, the *Lady Hammond* class mentioned in the last chapter. The *Laura*, instead of carrying her original rating of ten 18-pounder carronades, had but eight, the other two being replaced by two short 9-pounders, so she still carried her full rating, though less powerful than designed. She does not appear to have had a schooner rig, although we know that the *Barbara* and *Alphea* were schooners, and they were of the same model as the *Laura*. The *Diligent* was probably the usual pilot boat model and if so was about the same size as the *Laura*.

On Sept. 8, 1812, the *Diligent* fell in with the *Laura*, who had seized three American merchant ships and was in the act of capturing the fourth, with a boat. As soon as Lieutenant Hunter, the commander of the *Laura*, made out the *Diligent* to be an armed vessel, he recalled his boat and made sail for the *Diligent*. Some of the crew of the captured merchant ships knew the *Diligent*, and Lieutenant Hunter learned of her force from them.

At 3.55 P.M. the vessels were close together and the *Laura* opened fire, to which the *Diligent* responded. At four o'clock the vessels were alongside and the Americans were trying to manoeuvre to rake, which the *Laura* prevented by taking the wind out of the privateer's sails. At half past four the *Diligent* set her fore course (fore sail?) and endeavored to tack. The *Laura* tried to do the same, but due to the faint breeze both vessels missed stays and paying off before the wind, fought yard-arm to yard-arm. At 4.45 P.M. the *Laura's* peak halyards were shot away (this makes her appear to have been a sloop or cutter) and she fell off and grazed the port quarter of the *Diligent*, going ahead of her to leeward. The *Diligent* dropped astern and now being the best sailer of the two got on the *Laura's* weather quarter.

Up to this time, the vessels having been jockeyed about, their fire was not very effective, but now the *Diligent* took the wind out of the *Laura's* sails, ran her bowsprit over the starboard taffrail of the *Laura* and put her jibboom between the topping lifts and through the mainsail and having made fast in this position, attempted to board, in which, finally, at 4.55 P.M., she was successful and the *Laura* was captured.

The *Laura* was afterwards fitted out as a 12-gun privateer and renamed *Hebe*, but in April, 1813, was recaptured by a British squadron.

During the first year of the war, a Baltimore merchant ship, the *Hannibal*, was captured. This vessel is said to have been built in 1810 in Maryland, and was a very fast ship though little else is known of her history. After her capture she was taken into the Royal Navy and fitted out as a sloop of war and as such she was armed with twenty-two 32-pounder carronades and two 12-pounders, with a crew of 195 men. She was renamed the *Andromeda*, but was not in service very long, being sold out in 1816. There is a half model of this ship in The Science Museum at South Kensington, and her draught is presented here. Her sail plan is taken from her spar dimensions; the apparent single headsail, it should be added, is for calculation only and not an actual sail. She would have the usual ship's headsails of the period. She also carried a spritsail under her bowsprit, like the frigates of this date.

Her dimensions were 135 feet 6 inches long on the upper deck; 108 feet 6¼ inches length of the keel for tonnage; 37 feet 5½ inches extreme beam; 36 feet 11¼ inches moulded beam; 10 feet 11 inches depth of hold; and 809 4/94 tons burthen. She was a flush-decked ship. The draught shows her as originally fitted. Her spar dimensions were:

	MASTS Length Diam.		YARDS Length Diam.		Amount shorter than original spars MASTS Length	YARDS Length
Main	25 yds. 0 in.	x 23¼ in.	23 yds. 27 in.	x 16⅝ in.	4 ft. 9 in.	Jury
Topmast	15 0	x 14⅜	17 21	x 11	5 6	1 ft. 9 in.
Gallant	8 4	x 8	10 25	x 6⅜	5 5	6 0
Fore	23 0	x 21	20 26	x 14½	3 0	5 2
Topmast	13 15	x 14⅜	15 16	x 9¾	3 10	3 10
Gallant	7 6	x 7	9 16	x 5⅝	5 9	7 4
Mizzen	18 6	x 17	12 8	x 9 Gaffs	2 9	
Topmast	11 8	x 10⅛	11 26	x 6⅝	8 3	3 0
Gallant	6 6	x 5½	8 3	x 5¼	6 2	3 9
Bowsprit	16 0	x 23½	15 16	x 9¾	2 8	3 2
Cross jack yard			17 21	x 11		1 3
Jibboom	11 27	x 10¼			5 6	

The gaff is 2 feet 8 inches longer than the original.

The spar dimensions in this table are given in the usual Royal Navy style of the period, viz.: yards and inches, and the diameters in inches. The spars were shortened when the vessel was refitted and the amount of the reduction is shown in feet and inches. To obtain the original length of the spars, add the amount shortened to the spar dimensions listed in the table. There is a note on the draught to the effect that in the refitting, the mizzenmast was stepped on the lower deck instead of on the keelson, as originally fitted in the draught. The spars were shortened in the hounded lengths. The sail plan illustrates the original spar plan and not the Royal Navy spars.

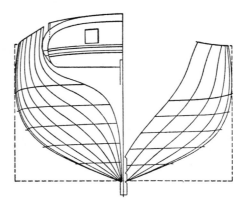

FIG. 16. LINES OF THE SHIP "HANNIBAL." BUILT AT BALTIMORE, 1810

This plan is of a very rare type, an American merchantman of the period of 1812. There are very few draughts in existence of American vessels of this date. Above the water she has the appearance of a French sloop of war of this period, but her underbody is an enlargement of the Baltimore clipper schooner, without as much rake to her sternport. The amount of deadrise is very great for a vessel of this size and rig. A comparison of this draught with that of the *Ann McKim*, another Baltimore ship of later date, shows some similarity in ideas, though the last named is far more extreme in type. The *Hannibal*, or *Andromeda*, has less drag to her keel, but the builder, like the builder of the *Ann McKim*, had the same general idea for a design of a fast ship. The *Hannibal*, we may therefore assume, is an example of a very early clipper ship. She is mentioned in James' "History of the Royal Navy," abstract 21, as being an extraordinarily fine ship and that her model should have been used for the class of ship-sloops to be built to oppose the American ship-sloops of the *Frolic* class.

Throughout this chapter there have been numerous references to the "pilot boat construction" privateer of 1812. Fortunately we have a few draughts, the best of which is the *Mosquidobit*, said to have been the American privateer *Lynx*. We know her history; something lacking with the others.

On April 3, 1813, Admiral Sir John Warren, in his flagship *San Domingo*, 74, and Read Admiral Cockburn's flagship *Marlborough*, 74, accompanied by the *Statira* and *Maidstone* frigates, and the *Mohawk* and *Fantome* brig-sloops, appeared off the Rappahannock River, where four

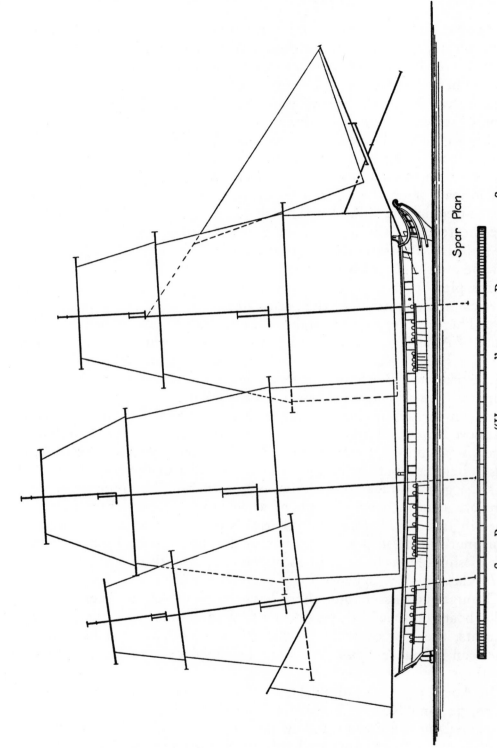

Spar Plan

Spar Plan of the ship "Hannibal," built at Baltimore in 1810

Andromeda (late Hannibal) as originally fitted

built at Baltimore 1810

Length of upper deck .... 135·6″
on keel for tonnage .... 108·6¼″
Breadth · Extreme .... 37·5⅝″
Moulded .... 36·11¼″
Depth in Hold .... 10·11″
Burthen in tons .... 809 54⁄94

Plymouth Yard
Sept. 10, 1812

American privateer schooners happened to be hiding. The schooners were the *Arab*, 7 guns and 45 men, Captain Fitch; the *Lynx*, 6 guns and 40 men, Captain Taylor; the *Racer*, 6 guns and 36 men, Captain Chaytor; and the *Dolphin*, 12 guns and 100 men, Captain Stafford, and the last named schooner was ready to sail on another marauding cruise. The others were in hiding, perhaps waiting to run the British blockade.

As soon as the British espied these schooners from their mastheads, they sent out a boat expedition under the command of Lieut. James Polkinghorne to cut them out. Unfortunately for the privateers it was calm, and the vessels could not aid one another, as they were too far apart for a good defense. Lieutenant Polkinghorne was therefore able to attack them separately, and the Arab was carried after a desperate defense by her crew. The *Lynx*, seeing there was no chance, hauled down her colors when summoned, but the *Racer*, in spite of this, made some defense, but was also carried. The English then turned the guns of these schooners on the *Dolphin*, probably towing them near enough for the fire to be effective, and after resisting for two hours, the *Dolphin* also struck.

This finished the careers of four active and powerful privateers, and while unfortunate from a patriotic standpoint, nevertheless this preserves for us a splendid amount of data on this class of vessel, as the *Dolphin*, *Racer* and *Lynx* were taken into the Royal Navy, the last two under the names *Shelbourne* and *Mosquidobit*. The *Shelbourne* was in at the capture of the American sloop of war *Frolic* in 1814, but the others apparently saw very little service.

The *Mosquidobit* was sent to England and her lines were taken off and a draught was made May 10, 1816, a copy of which is here reproduced. Her dimensions were: length on the deck, 94 feet 7 inches; length of the keel for tonnage, 73 feet 1¼ inches; breadth, extreme, 24 feet; breadth, moulded, 23 feet 8 inches; depth of hold, 10 feet 3 inches; burthen in tons, 223 91/94. The plan was drawn by N. S. Diddams at the Portsmouth Yard. This is a very interesting plan of a very fine privateer schooner, with square topsails forward, as may be assumed from her deadeyes on the channels. The only thing lacking to complete our satisfaction is the spar dimensions, which unfortunately are not to be found.

Now that we have the history of this schooner, let us turn to the draught. First we see that she is a rather large vessel, with very raking stem and sternpost and with a great deal of drag to the keel. The next noticeable particular is the amount of deadrise, about 30°. Her bilges are slack, as we have found other vessels of the type to have. Her spars rake very sharply aft and both masts rake the same. She has very little sheer and a very short and small head for the gammoning. The lack of decoration is noticeable, there are no frills or gingerbread work. She has high bulwarks and a very plain transom with two ports in it. She apparently steered with a tiller, from the position of her rudder head. She has seven ports and if she carried her full rating would have had at least twelve guns and probably thirteen, including a traversing piece.

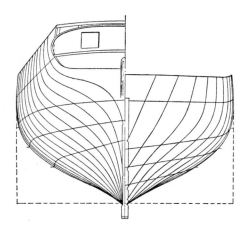

The waterlines are sharp and she has a straight entrance and a very long, sharp run. There can be no question that this vessel was very fast; her lines are extremely fine. She is much deeper than the *Flying Fish*, but shows some of that vessel's characteristics. Her inboard profile needs no explanation and so we will reconstruct her deck plan. Beginning at the transom, going forward, we have the rud-

FIG. 17 — LINES OF H. M. SCHOONER
"MUSQUIDOBIT"

der head and a tiller; then a small hatch into the run, next the capstan, and here it should be stated that nearly all of the privateer schooners had their capstans right aft. Next we have a hatch leading to the main cabin, then the pumps, then another hatch, apparently leading to the magazine, and still another hatch leading to the officers' quarters. All the hatches are small.

At the foot of the mainmast is a bitt supported by two long knees, the foremast also having the same type of bitt. Between the main- and foremasts are two hatches, the larger one, aft, leads into the main hold and crews' quarters, and the smaller one, forward, is the galley hatch with a chimney coming up through it. Forward of the foremast there is a riding bitt, a small forecastle hatch, and then the heel of the bowsprit. There is a knee, right up in the eyes of her, over the bowsprit, to strengthen the bulwarks forward, and there was probably a grating on top of this. The catheads go through the bulwarks, not over them, and this construction appears in *Dominica*. The catheads were apparently sawed out of a "natural crook" and had a cant beside, so as to back a bulwark stanchion alongside the foremast gun-port.

This vessel is worth very close study, as she is a fine example of the general type of privateer schooners built on the pilot boat model during the War of 1812. This beautiful vessel is an example of the highest development of the Baltimore Clipper, not extreme, as compared to latter craft, but the natural development from the class of vessels represented by the "Virginia-built Privateer" and the *Swift*.

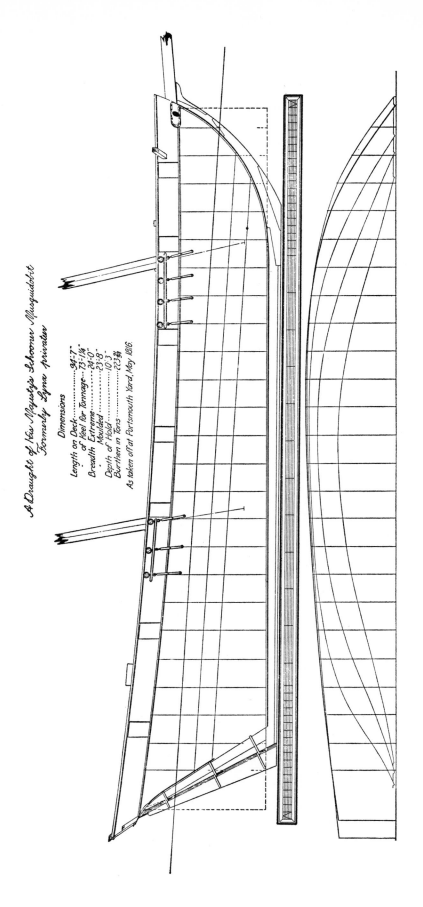

A Draught of His Majesty's Schooner Musquidobit
Formerly Lynx privateer

Dimensions

Length on Deck............94'-7"
of Keel for Tonnage....73'-1¼"
Breadth Extreme..........24'-0"
        Moulded..........23'-8"
Depth of Hold.............10'-3"
Burthen in Tons...........223¾

As taken off at Portsmouth Yard, May 1816.

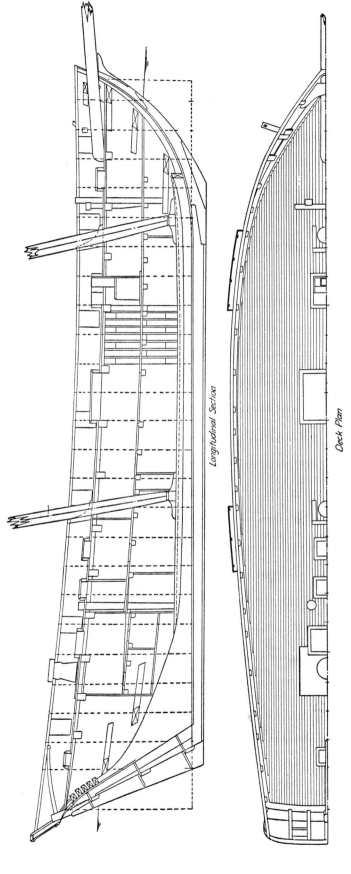

Longitudinal Section

Deck Plan

Longitudinal Section and Deck Plan of His Majesty's Schooner "Musquidobit," as taken off at Portsmouth Yard, May, 1816

The next vessel we shall study will be H. M. schooner *Alban*. This vessel had her lines taken off and a draught made at the Plymouth Yard on May 19, 1817. She was a large clipper schooner of 252 75/94 tons burthen, with

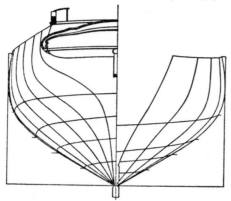

FIG. 18 — LINES OF H. M. SCHOONER "ALBAN"

a length on the range of deck of 94 feet 4½ inches; length of the keel for tonnage, 78 feet 6⅞ inches; breadth, extreme, 24 feet 7⅛ inches; breadth, moulded, 24 feet 2⅝ inches, and depth of hold, 10 feet 6 inches. She is very near the dimensions of the *Mosquidobit*, but in appearance is an altogether different vessel. While nothing certain is known of her history, she is supposed to have been a captured American privateer, and the date of her draught strengthens this supposition. She was pierced for eighteen guns and would be rated as a sixteen-gun schooner. While she cannot be identified as yet, nevertheless she is of interest as an example of the type under discussion, as she has the same elements of design as the *Mosquidobit*, and like that vessel is a very handsome craft.

The draught presented shows her load and light waterlines, which are rarely shown on the draughts. Her stern is very graceful and there is a moulding running the full length of vessel and along the top of the head, ending in a spiral at the extremity of the head. She has very raking ends, though not quite so great as those of the *Mosquidobit*. In deck arrangement she differs from the last named vessel somewhat as her galley is forward of the foremast, her pumps are forward of the mainmast, and there are other minor differences. Her catheads go over the top of her bulwarks and she has a long chock on each side of her stem. It will be noticed that she is fitted for twelve sweeps, six on a side. The oar-ports are between the gun-ports and are covered like those of *Flying Fish*. She also has stern davits overhanging her transom. The transom also has some decoration, and as a whole she has more finish than the *Mosquidobit*. She steered with a tiller.

Her spar dimensions are given and so we have her sail plan. These dimensions, like the others, are in yards and inches. Whether or not this is a cutdown rig is a matter of speculation. The hull is not as sharp as that of the *Mosquidobit*, but the lines are very good. This also must have been a fast schooner. The Royal Navy only bought in vessels that fulfilled the following specifications, in order of their importance: good construction; speed; ability to carry guns and handiness; and the schooners whose lines were tak-

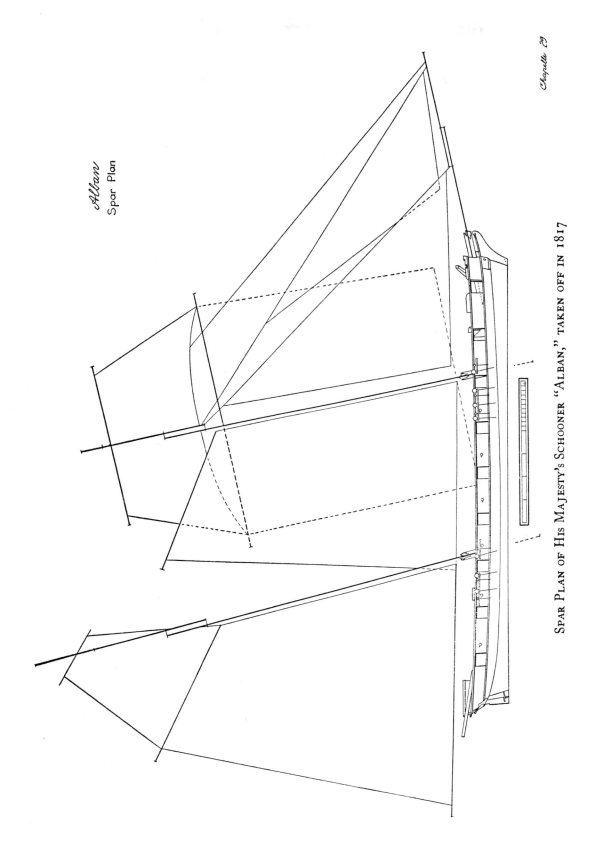

Alban
Spar Plan

Chapelle 29

SPAR PLAN OF HIS MAJESTY'S SCHOONER "ALBAN," TAKEN OFF IN 1817

A Draught of His Majesty's Schooner Allan

Length on deck .... 94'·4½"
" of keel for tonnage .... 78'·6⅞"
Breadth Extreme .... 24'·7⅞"
" Moulded .... 24'·2⅝"
Depth of Hold .... 10'·6"
Burthen in Tons .... 252 75⁄94

Plymouth Yard. May 19. 1817

Load
Light

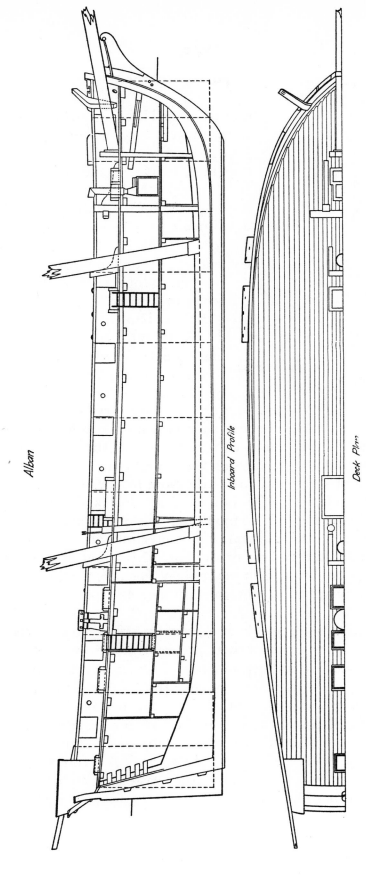

Alban

Inboard Profile

Deck Plan

INBOARD PROFILE AND DECK PLAN OF HIS MAJESTY'S SCHOONER "ALBAN," PLYMOUTH YARD, MAY 19, 1817

en off between 1814 and 1818 were usually those of American privateers that possessed these virtues.

The schooner that is next to be discussed is H. M. schooner *Grecian* whose

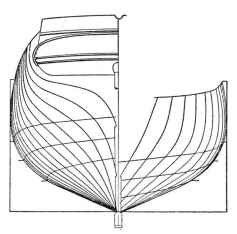

FIG. 19 — LINES OF H. M. SCHOONER "GRECIAN"

lines were taken off and a draught made at the Portsmouth Yard, on May 10, 1816, by N. S. Diddams. She was about the size of the *Mosquidobit*, and a schooner of 224 31/94 tons burthen. Her other dimensions are: length of the deck, 95 feet 1 inch; length of the keel for tonnage, 74 feet 3 inches; breadth, extreme, 23 feet 10 inches; breadth, moulded, 23 feet 5 inches; and depth of hold, 10 feet 5 inches. The *Grecian* apparently had a double-topsail rig, as her after channel has more deadeyes than the forward one, though this may not be conclusive. The first thing about this schooner that strikes the eye is the extreme rake of her ends and her very broken sheer line. She is a long, very low-sided schooner with a great deal of drag to her keel, and the usual raking masts. Her stern is wide and powerful and her entrance is long and sharp. The waterlines on the draught are fairing lines; her load line is marked and she would go a little more by the stern than the uppermost waterline indicates. Her bulwarks are low and the gun-ports are arched above them. There is no moulding or cap rail along the top of the bulwark and this is most unusual. Her waterlines are very sharp and she has very little flare to the forward sections. This vessel, while in the Royal Navy, had a reputation of being extremely good in turning to windward. Her bobstay iron is very high on the cutwater and her bowsprit was probably rather short.

We have her inboard profile and from it have reconstructed her deck plan. On each of her quarters there are small structures, sometimes called round houses. One was a storeroom and officers' toilet, the other was so divided that part was a meat pantry, and the remainder the crew's toilet. The space between was open, and when in the Royal Navy a raised poop deck was built just above the top of the rudder head, running forward to where the stern perpendicular, projected up, would intersect it. The forward edge of the bulkhead closing the poop deck's fore end was the extension of this perpendicular, and the tiller passed through an opening in it. She probably did not have this when originally fitted as a privateer, so it is

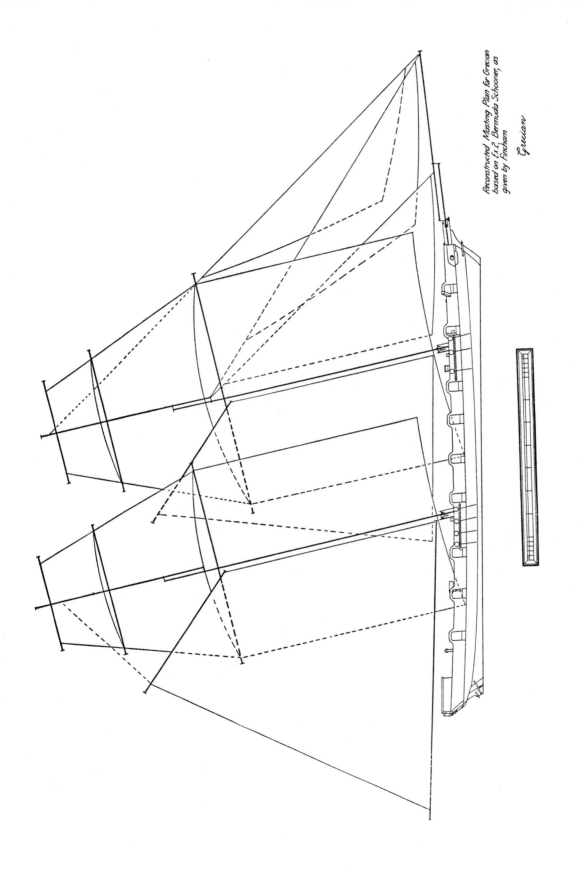

Reconstructed Masting Plan for Grecian based on Ex. 2, Bermuda Schooner, as given by Fincham

Grecian

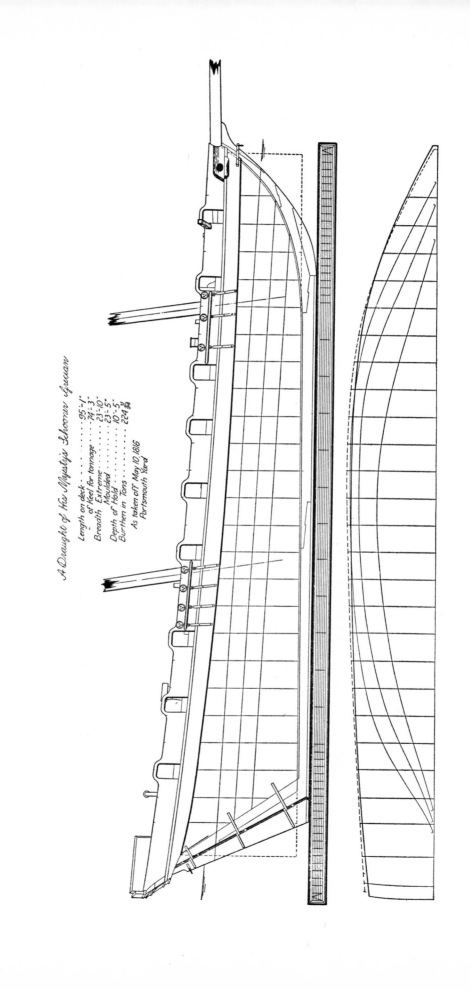

A Draught of His Majesty's Schooner Grecian

Length on deck . . . . 95'-1"
  " of Keel for tonnage . . 74'-3"
Breadth Extreme . . . . . 23'-10"
  Moulded . . . . . . 23'-5"
Depth of Hold . . . . . . 10'-5"
Burthen in Tons 224 31/94

As taken off May 10, 1816
Portsmouth Yard

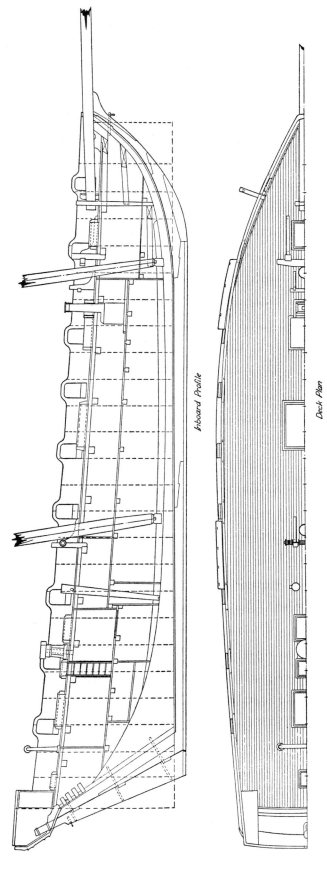

Inboard Profile

Deck Plan

INBOARD PROFILE AND DECK PLAN OF HIS MAJESTY'S SCHOONER "GRECIAN," TAKEN OFF MAY 10, 1816

not shown on the draught. Just forward of the hatch opening into her run, there is a main sheet horse, apparently mounted on two upright circular pillars or supports. This may not be the main sheet horse, but if not, it is difficult to identify it. Its position seems to be rather far forward for this fitting, but if the vessel steered with a tiller, such a position might be necessary.

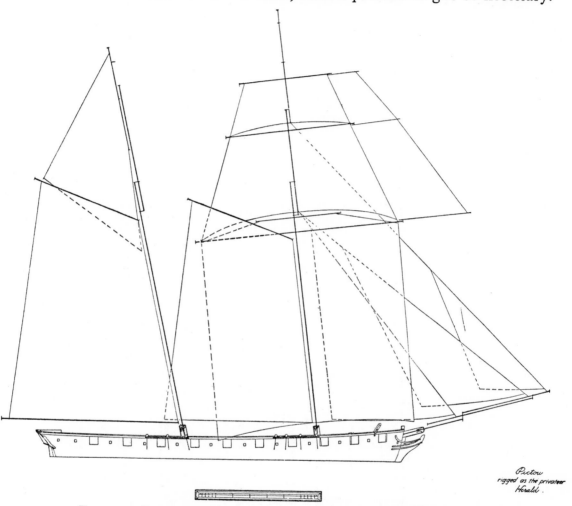

FIG. 20 — SCHOONER "PICTOU," RIGGED AS THE PRIVATEER "HERALD"

The *Grecian's* deck plan differs but little from the *Mosquidobit's*, and the only detail that needs special attention is the galley chimney, which has a revolving cover.

The original name of this vessel is unknown, as the records do not apparently give her privateering name. Her history in the Royal Navy shows that she was employed largely in the West Indies, until into the 1820's, when she was sold out. About that time she was rigged as a three-masted schooner and when in private hands had a short career in the slave trade and also did a little smuggling, it is said. Her sail plan is a reconstruction from Fincham's rules and dimensions.

Before leaving these Royal Navy schooners, let us take one more sample, the *Pictou*. This is a large schooner of nearly 300 tons, supposed to have been an ex-privateer, but like most of the others, there is nothing certain known of her capture. Her length on the range of deck was 101 feet 5 inches, unusually long; length of the keel for tonnage, 85 feet 6½ inches; breadth, extreme, 25 feet 7⅝ inches; moulded beam, 25 feet 2⅝ inches; depth of hold 10 feet ½ inch; and

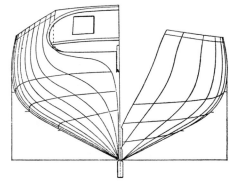

FIG. 21 — LINES OF H. M. SCHOONER "PICTOU"

her burthen 299 tons. Her lines were taken off and a draught made at the Portsmouth Yard, March 22, 1815, and signed by N. S. Diddams. There are pencil marks on the body plan of the original draught showing a proposed design along the lines of this vessel, but with a change in the sections forward, consisting of hipping them out at the load waterline. This would have made her fuller forward, and there were some more lines at the stern indicating that, in this proposed design, the load waterline aft was not to have the reverse curve shown in the draught. Apparently no design was made, however.

This vessel is marked by less rake to the ends than the others; the drag of her keel, aft, is quite marked, as is the amount of deadrise. She is quite sharp forward with a long easy run, very little sheer, 10 ports (18 guns?), 22 sweeps, 11 oar-ports on a side, long head with headrails and knees. Her oar-ports are square and her channels are at the top of her bulwarks. Her masts do not have as much rake as most privateers had.

The original draught had the following title: "A Draught of His Majesty's Schooner *Pictou* (late *Zebra*) as taken off." There is no record of a privateer named *Zebra* hailing from any American port so this could not have been her name in this service, but an earlier name that may have been given her in the Royal Navy.

In conclusion it should be added that there are very many references to this schooner as being American built, and in service during the last days of the war. She is hardly of the pilot boat type, but may easily have been one of the very numerous captured American privateers, sailing from northern

A Draught of His Majesty's Schooner Pictou

late "Zebra" as taken off.

Length on deck	101'.5"
" of keel for tonnage	85'.6¾
Breadth Extreme	25'.7½
" Moulded	25'.2½
Depth in Hold	10'.0½
Burthen in Tons	299

Portsmouth Yard
Mar. 22, 1815

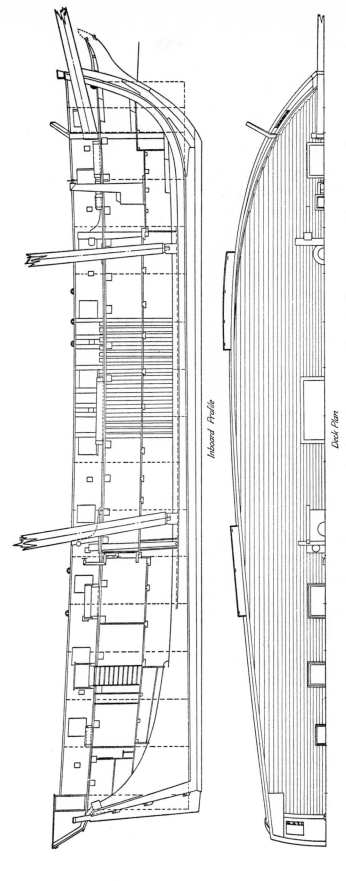

Inboard Profile

Deck Plan

Inboard Profile and Deck Plan of His Majesty's Schooner "Pictou," taken off March 22, 1815

ports, such as Salem, Boston or New York. As all evidence seems to indicate that she was an ex-American privateer, we may safely assume that she is another variation of the type during the period under discussion.

Now that we know what the Baltimore Clipper of this period looked like, we can speculate as to the influence that captured privateers may have had on the Royal Navy. The mere fact that draughts were made of any of them showed that they were considered unusually fine craft, as of the many hundreds of vessels captured or bought, and taken into the Royal Navy between 1770 and 1815, very few had their lines taken off. It is possible that future research may add a few more to the available list, but so far, vessels of this class with ratings below the 16-gun brigs, are very scarce. The numerous pencil notations on the draughts discussed show that much time and thought was spent in study of them, for use in designing later vessels in the Royal Navy. The fact that the vessels were very fast is apparent, and perhaps this had more to do with the interest of the Naval constructors than anything else. Many of the elements exhibited in these schooners appear in later small cruisers of the Royal Navy, particularly the small schooners built in the West Indies, at Nassau, Jamaica, and Bermuda, during the suppression of the slave trade, say, from 1820 to 1835. Many brigs built for the Royal Navy after the War of 1812, had certain characteristics that connect them with these schooners, yet one must not be too enthusiastic in arriving at this opinion, for by 1832, the great English naval constructor Symonds carried the deadrise idea to its greatest development, and rather to an extreme, in working out theories which appear to have been original with him.

Before leaving this discussion, we must remark upon the good fortune that constructors at that time were interested in this type. It is from their draughts that the best of our information is now obtained, as early drawings of vessels of the United States Navy are not obtainable, nor are the drawings of privateers available elsewhere.

From what information we can obtain from the list of American privateers, the size of a vessel cannot be judged by the number of guns she carried. Thus, the *Mosquidobit* and the *Lynx* only carried six guns, though rated at twelve guns and probably thirteen. We have enough data, however, to know that a great many of the earlier schooners were but about fifty feet long, but during the last half of the war, the 95-foot schooners became popular, and some, like the *Harlequin*, ran up to 323 tons, English measurement. This vessel must have been well over 100 feet on deck, and she was certainly larger than the *Pictou*, if James' description is correct.

Another matter that seems important is the fact that none of these privateers had much decoration, and it seems probable that most of them had merely a gammon-knee head, without headrails, fashion, or trail boards or knees. Figureheads were not often used, although the *Young Teazer* is said to have had an alligator for a figurehead, and the *Thomas*, of Portsmouth, had a wildcat, according to Canadian accounts. Some of the privateers had a little decoration on the transom, spiral mouldings and raised trim, but little or no carving seems to have been used. The whole design motif was strictly of utility. Beauty, so far as finish went, was little considered. The privateer schooners had less decoration than men-of-war of the same period, for even gun-brigs had headrails and often figureheads. In fact the only types of vessels that refrained from carved decorations, other than these schooners, were the famous English cutters, and the French armed luggers.

The first American privateers to get to sea, in 1812, were largely pilot boats of small size, lightly armed, but strong enough to capture the average armed merchantman. As the war progressed, the English increased the armament of their vessels, which necessitated an increase in size and power in the privateers. Some of them were equal to a sloop-of-war, or a gun-brig. This necessary increase in size brought out the large pilot boat model schooners represented by *Grecian* and *Mosquidobit*, as well as others of similar build. This larger class, the result of a study of small vessels of the same general type produced earlier in the war, were the highest development of the Baltimore Clipper, as all around vessels. After the end of the war there was a degeneration of the type, due mainly to the uses it was put to. This degeneration, if we may call it that, developed a vessel that was very fast under certain conditions, faster than the privateer — pilot boat type, but less able, and in no way equal in general ability, gun carrying, sail carrying, and seaworthiness, to the privateer pilot boat class.

The list of privateers of the War of 1812 brings out another interesting point — the wide range of construction of the type of vessel. Baltimore and its immediate vicinity seems to have contributed a larger number than any other district, but New York, New Bedford, Salem, Boston and Portsmouth, N. H., built a very large number of pilot boat model privateers. In the South, Charleston, New Orleans, Savannah, Portsmouth, Va., and Norfolk, Va., built similar vessels. This spread of the type was due to war conditions, no doubt, but it seems a little surprising. This is particularly true in New England where fishing schooners and Chebacco boats were in use. Some of these Chebacco boats are said to have been fast sailers, but none are mentioned as privateers. This may have been due to their small size, but it would seem possible to enlarge the type for that service. Very few fishing schooners seem to have been employed. It is possible that the lack of speed was the chief handicap of these craft, so the pilot boat type was adapted for privateering. Sloops were very popular in New England waters, and we find these fitted out for privateering. These were traders and were, perhaps, quite fast. As an additional note, there are references to pilot boat model vessels with sloop rigs. These appear to have been keel sloops (centerboards apparently were not in use until after the war) and were rather large and fast vessels. It would be interesting to know if they were anything like the Bermuda sloops in appearance.

In the literature of privateering there are some references to 24-hour runs, but they are rather indefinite. The ship *America* privateer made some very good 24-hour runs. She was known to have been a very fast vessel. From log books it would seem that some of the schooners could do better than twelve knots. *The Liverpool Packet*, alias *Young Teazer's Ghost, Portsmouth Packet*, etc., sailed better than 250 miles in 24 hours, and as this vessel was only 53 feet long, she must have been exceptionally fast. In very few cases were any of the privateers under press of canvas for a full 24 hours, except when chased, and when it would usually be under unfavorable conditions, such as light airs, and so the distance run was often not very great. Some of these privateers were captured by Royal Navy cruisers after a two to six days' chase; one, in fact, was taken after an eleven-day chase.

The number of American privateer schooners and brigs captured by the Royal Navy cruisers was large, but in the majority of captures the privateer was badly handled or unlucky through loss of spars or sails. Often, too, the privateer got too close to a man-of-war before discovering her identity or ran too close during fog or darkness. A very large number of the larger privateers were captured by cutting out expeditions, a favorite and highly dangerous pastime of both English and American tars of this period.

It was during the War of 1812 that we see a change in the topsail schooner. Most of the topsail schooners were square-rigged on the foremast only. Some carried a square topsail on the mainmast and this is the double-topsail schooner. Both rigs often had topgallants and royals above these topsails, particularly the large privateers. These rigs were very popular and the double-topsail rig had many of the advantages of the brig in naval warfare. At first the fore and aft sails were the outstanding part of the rig, but at the end of the war many schooners were built that were very nearly brigs, due to the increase in size of the square sails and reductions in the fore and aft sails. This rig was listed in the various Navy Lists as "brig-schooner," and was particularly popular in the Royal Navy as a rig for the captured Baltimore Clippers taken into service. This is possibly the rig carried by the *Grecian* and similar schooners. The "brig-schooner" rig eventually reverts

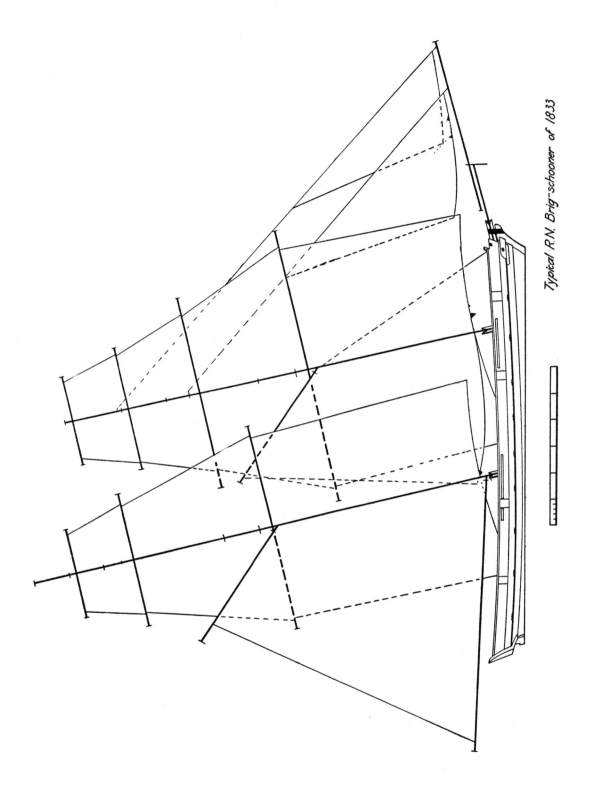

Typical R.N. Brig-schooner of 1833

to what is practically the brig or rather brigantine and then disappeared. By 1830 the fore and aft sails were so small as to be of little use, and the lower masts became rather short, as in most brigs, which usually resulted in rerigging them as true brigs or brigantines. The square topsail rig, with square topsails, topgallants and often royals on the foremast only remained in use until the end of the fighting sailing craft, as a part of the schooner rig. Schooners, except American privateer schooners, were all small, in the navies at least, and of course there were variations in method of masting and rigging each individual vessel. Certain proportions, however, seem to have been in force for length of masts, yards and booms, and these proportions related oftenest to extreme beam. The proportions give rather long masts for large vessels and these masting rules may be found in the Appendix of this volume.

The accompanying reproduction of the painting of a Virginia pilot boat off Cape Henry shows the small schooner rig used on the Chesapeake and the general appearance of all of the small pilot schooners. This rig does not seem to have had any square sails when in the pilot service, but from the remarks and descriptions of writers who were eyewitnesses of privateer actions during the war, we know that when privateering, they carried a square sail, and sometimes a square topsail. It is probable that only boats of over 60 foot length on deck would carry square topsails, as a rule. However, even the smallest could carry a square sail at sea, as is now being done in small ocean-going sailing yachts. This square sail was narrow at the yard and broader at the foot.

While we have no builder's sail plans for this type of schooner, during the years 1812 to 1820, we have spar dimensions of vessels built just after the war from which it will be possible to reconstruct the pilot schooner rig of that time. There is also in existence a set of drawings of a pilot schooner of 1838, designed by Isaac Webb, the *John McKeon*.* These may be found in "Plans of Wooden Ships," by Isaac Webb. This schooner, 78 feet 0 inches stem to rudder, 20 feet 7 inches moulded beam, and 7 feet 6 inches depth of hold, is a shallow schooner with rounded stem, counter stern, extreme deadrise, slack bilges, and rather great beam. Her sail plan shows very long masts. The foremast is roughly 70 feet, deck to head, and the mainmast is about the same. The gaffs are short, the main boom overhangs the stern about one-third of its length and the foresail has no boom. There is a lug head topsail on the mainmast. Of special interest to us is the square sail on the foremast. The yard is about sixty feet above the deck, and nearly 31 feet long. The fore-topmast is very short; the hoist of the square topsail

* Copy in the New York Public Library.

is about 18 feet 6 inches and the topsail yard is only about 9 feet long, al-most a club. The sail itself is somewhat like a raffee. The foot of the square sail is nearly 60 feet long, or about twice the length of the head. This rig seems to have been the standard pilot rig, with one or two headsails. A large jib, a flying jib and jib topsail were used on the *McKeon*. This rig, with little variation, was in use during the War of 1812, and was probably the rig used by the pilot boat privateer.

The brig rig needs little explanation. Except for longer and more raking spars it differed little from the rig of the man-of-war brig. The privateer brig, however, was often "over hatted." The loss of the pilot boat model brig *Arrow*, of New York, was accounted for by the statement that her spars were very long and her hull very sharp. It was thought that she was either run under (pitch poled) or capsized in a squall, for she was never heard from again. This fault of the Baltimore Clipper brig seems to have been uncorrected throughout its existence.

There are numerous instances of schooners and brigs being driven under while in chase of an enemy or while being pursued. This was true of the Baltimore Clipper and was due to fullness in the forward sections. This type of hull form tends to bore or fall by the head when driven hard, which, added to the lever of the masts and press of sail, tended to drive them un-der, headforemost. Man-of-war brigs of 1800-1850 were particularly li-able to this. The 10-gun brigs of that time were known as "coffins" be-cause of their tendency in this direction. One Royal Navy gun-brig, while running off before a gale, pitch poled, or capsized, end over end, alongside a ship-of-the-line. All that was found floating was a sailor's cap. Baltimore Clipper brigs were more prone to this than the schooners, as brigs, for some reason, were fuller in their waterlines forward than schooners, and often had their greatest beam further forward. This was perhaps due to the weight of the foremast and yards, together with the long bowsprit, jibboom and fly-ing jibboom so popular in the brigs of this period. In order to get displace-ment forward, to carry this weight, the forward sections were filled out, and the greatest beam moved forward. Of course, this was not true of all Bal-timore Clipper brigs, but it was the case in many vessels. Apparently some of the schooners must have had the same fault, though no plan available shows this. This fault among brigs was particularly noticeable in men-of-war brigs, both in the United States and Royal Navies. A casual inspection of draughts of Royal Navy brigs, from 1810 to 1850, in the collection of the Admiral-ty, shows that a large number of them trimmed by the head, that is, the wa-terline at the bow was higher than designed. To overcome this tendency the bows were filled out, with doubtful results, so far as safety was concerned.

Capsizing was generally due to one of two things—over sparring, or, when being chased, the practice of throwing overboard the lee guns. With a small vessel, the weight of the battery was no small item in its displacement, and if the lee battery went overboard and for any reason the vessel had to luff or change tacks, there was great danger of capsizing. There is one instance of a French schooner with her battery in this condition, capsizing to windward by being sailed into the lee formed by a ship-of-the-line.

Over sparring was always common and the clipper schooners and brigs built for the privateering and naval services had this fault, almost without exception. But they were safe if in the hands of an officer who was acquainted with their handling; in the hands of an unskilled commander, however, their antics, as described by eyewitnesses, were hair-raising to say the least. These long-sparred vessels, in spite of this, do not seem to have suffered capsizing as often as one would have expected. Few capsized under way, but quite a number did at anchor. The United States schooner *Alligator* capsized, it is said, in this manner in Charleston Harbor. Men-of-war schooners were particularly bad, in this respect, as the number lost through capsizing at anchor, was large. Most of them crossed yards on their foremasts at least, and the weight of the spars with the necessary rigging, the weight of their heavy batteries high up, combined often with a lack of ballast, due to too light a displacement to carry the load put on their decks, all tended to make them very tender. While lying at anchor in a strong tidal current, a hard squall might come up against the tide and as the wind could not force the vessel against tide, the ship would swing across it. The force of the tide on her keel and the pressure of wind on her tophamper would then heel her down to the danger point, and beyond. As the vessel had no way, she could not be brought head to the wind, and over she would go, fill, and sink. Few of the privateers did this trick, for their lack of top weight saved them, though their spars were as long or longer than the man-of-war schooners. However, some of the pilot and opium clippers built after the war were guilty of similar tricks.

By the end of the war, the desire for extreme speed, so marked among the owners of the Baltimore Clipper privateers and merchant craft, naturally led the builders to all kinds of extremes, particularly in the smaller types. These extreme designs were also built in the larger classes later. The speed was increased on certain points of sailing, at the expense of speed on others.

The ship-builders of the period of the War of 1812 were not naval architects but a practical knowledge arrived at through constant building of fast vessels and a continual study of those elements necessary in a fast sailing schooner or brig, gave them the ability to design and build vessels that had a very high rate of speed combined with seaworthiness. Having no method of putting their designs on paper and checking the elements of such designs, either mathematically or by the eye, they were often led, like the later yacht modelers and builders, to great extremes, due to the fact that the tendency of such a builder is to attribute speed of sailing to certain elements, as in the clipper schooners, deadrise, cut-away ends and raking spars were considered to be absolutely necessary in a fast vessel.

During the period just discussed, the Baltimore type reached the height of its natural development, which is merely a matter of refinement, and with the passing of this development an artificial improvement in design began consisting usually in exaggerating certain features of the type, such as deadrise, draft, beam, or by cutting the ends away even more. Of course this last statement is mere generalizing and it does not follow that just after the war all of the schooners and brigs built on Baltimore lines were extreme, nor faulty in design; but the trend of design, if it may be called that, is in the direction of extremes.

Certain lessons were learned by the builders of privateers that they often carried to great extremes. The first was the matter of deadrise. Many of the fast pilot boat model privateers were built with great deadrise, and some with a slight hollow in the floor. These vessels were found to be fast, particularly to windward, and in later boats this hollow deadrise became more marked. The question as to whether hollow deadrise helps speed is often a matter of argument, as so much depends upon the other features of the model. Generally speaking, it seems safe to state that no one feature of the design of a fast sailing vessel is the sole reason for her speed. The fairness of her form, the balance of her centers of buoyancy, sail, gravity and lateral area, the position and shape of her mid-section or section of greatest beam are all important, but like deadrise and hollow floors, no one of them can alone make a fast sailer. The secret of hull form, which can be seen in many of the Baltimore schooners in the Royal Navy service, seems to have been the rather long run, fair diagonals and buttock lines and refined model, rather than either deadrise or hollow floors. The centers of buoyancy, gravity, lateral area, etc., in such forms, automatically align themselves. Sharp waterlines, comparatively speaking, also come in automatically, if the buttock and diagonal lines are to be fair and easy. All this, again, is generalization, but these views are expressed more to draw attention to the excellent lines of these vessels rather than to enter into a purely theoretical and technical discussion of design. Before going further into the progress of the type, a comparison of the *Mosquidobit*, *Grecian* and *Flying Fish* with modern cruising schooner yachts, will show that waterlines, particularly the shape of the load waterlines have changed but little. It is possible some of these Baltimore Clippers, with modern sail cutting and ballasting, would be superior in speed to the general run of cruising yachts, particularly in open waters.

CHAPTER V

THE SLAVE TRADE

THE history of the slave trade and the story of the Baltimore Clipper are closely related, after about 1820. Before the declaration of peace and the exile of Napoleon, little was done toward the actual suppression of the slave trade, in spite of the fact that most of the Powers had agreed to limitations and control of the trade. As soon as peace again settled upon the world, the Great Powers turned their attention to regulating the slavers and traders. By that time, also, many had begun to eye the slave trade with distaste, in part due to the publication of eyewitnesses' accounts of cruelty on board slaving vessels, and these people soon raised their voices in protest, with the result that the governments were finally forced to forbid the transportation of slaves. England had freed all the slaves in her Colonies before the end of the Napoleonic Wars, and in consequence of the Abolition Movement had entered into treaties for the complete suppression of the trade. This movement finally reached the United States and this government also became, on paper, at least, a party to these treaties.

The Royal Navy, freed from war service, turned its full attention to the slave trade in the West Indies and on the African stations, and for this service the fastest brigs and schooners that the navy possessed were sent out as well as frigates and sloops of war. Beside these faster men-of-war, the navy stationed slower craft to assist, if necessary. This system became more and more effective and when the United States finally began in earnest to live up to the treaties concerning the slave trade, slavery distinctly began to decline.

Beginning, at about the year 1820, the ships of the Royal Navy pursued the traders along the African coast, on the Middle Passage, and throughout the West Indies. By 1830 the cruisers had made it very risky for slavers to do any trading, and by the late 1840's, slave trading became almost impossible. The first attempts at suppressing the slave trade actually began at about the end of the Napoleonic Wars but did not reach a full measure of success until about 1828, when the force of what was practically a blockade of the African coast and the West Indies was felt. From then until about 1845, the Royal Navy cruisers were very active and had many brushes with armed slavers. By 1845, the Powers had practically closed the markets for slavers, as well as restricted sources of supply. While there were intermittent outbreaks of slaving up to the time of the American Civil War, the trade was dead commercially by 1850.

Until the end of the Napoleonic Wars, slaving ships were generally large and often under government supervision. While of some importance to evade enemy cruisers, speed was not the leading factor in the design. Capacity, comfort, and handiness were of far greater importance, and they were run with the same type of crews and officers that were employed in the merchant marine.

When treaties were enforced, slaving became a desperate game. No longer were the traders protected and their ships and property respected. Cruisers were on the hunt for them and since they were outlawed, their own kind often preyed upon them. Under these circumstances, only fast-sailing vessels were wanted — none others could exist very long. The end of the War of 1812 left shipowners with ex-privateers and ship-builders with letter-of-marque or privateer vessels on the stocks. The slave traders were acquainted with the privateering type which apparently had been in use as tenders on the African coast before 1810, and they bought them up or contracted for vessels to be built on the same models for use as slavers. Just after the war times were hard for the ship-builders and about 1818, some went to Havana, to build slavers there. After 1820, the Royal Navy cruisers becoming more and more active, the demand for Baltimore Clippers increased.

It is not our purpose to enter into a detailed history of the slave trade, but merely to touch upon certain phases of its suppression and to indicate by this activity the changing influences of the design of the Baltimore Clippers, for builders naturally studied the conditions under which slavers operated. This meant that vessels were built to sail best with the usual weights carried by slavers; to sail best in the weather conditions of the Middle Passage and the West Indies; and to handle with slaver crews. Of course, the interior of the hull was laid out for the accommodation of slaves and provisions. The results of construction for this trade may be summarized as follows: increase of deadrise and draft, sharper waterlines, longer spars, less displacement, use of more light sails, unencumbered decks, smaller and fewer deck openings, and lighter construction.

The increase of deadrise on slaving ships over that of the privateers may be explained by observing the conditions of the waters frequented by the

CAPTURE OF SPANISH SLAVER "DOLORES," APRIL 4, 1816, OFF THE CONGO
BY H.M. BRIG "FERRET"

From a colored lithograph, after the painting by W. J. Huggins, in the Macpherson Collection

THE SLAVER "L'ANTONIO," WITH OTHER BLACK CRAFT, LYING IN BONNY RIVER

From a colored lithograph published in London, in 1841, in the Macpherson Collection

VIEW OF NEW ORLEANS, LOUISIANA, FROM ABOVE THE MIDDLE FERRY

From a colored aquatint, published in 1841, after a painting by William J. Bennett, in the
Macpherson Collection

slavers. The privateer had to work coastwise, often in rather shoal water, and had to be fitted to cruise in all climes and weather; whereas the slaver, as a rule, worked only in certain deep harbors, and in the open Atlantic. Her passages were made in tropic and semi-tropic weather, usually in the northern trades, where steady winds and rolling seas usually existed. Bad storms were infrequent, in fact, a perusal of the logs shows a prevalence of flat calms and light weather with occasional squalls. Vessels fitted for this type of sailing were of necessity light weather flyers and the builders designed them to be at their best under these conditions. Increase of draft, through greater deadrise, was not objectionable if the speed and sail carrying capacity could be increased. Light weather sailing called for light sails, kites, and longer spars with attendant increase of sail areas. But these vessels also had to stand up in hard squalls and carry sail. Therefore it was both natural and easy for builders to reach the conclusion that lower ballast was the best way out of their designing difficulties. Baltimore builders, too, had experimented timidly in this direction when building their pilot boat model privateers during the War of 1812, and now, having a free hand in this direction, they soon reached extreme proportions.

In the course of their experiments they found that if their deadrise was great, and the vessel had a straight, rising floor, it necessitated too great a proportion of ballast and even then the vessel often lacked stability. They overcame this fault by building later slave ships with slightly hollow floors and harder bilges.

This increase in deadrise with other changes in shape of the mid-section, generally speaking, increased the weatherliness of the schooners and brigs built for this trade, but usually at the expense of running qualities. However, during this period the Baltimore Clipper had reverted to her original status, of being the pursued rather than the pursuer, so she could pick a slant best suited to show her sailing qualities. The privateer had to be more of an all-around sailer in order to pursue as well as be pursued.

The increase of deadrise naturally brought out sharper waterlines and since the weight of guns did not have to be allowed for, displacement, in proportion to length and beam, became gradually less. Another thing that made the slave ship an ideal vessel in which to carry out experiments was the fact that her light condition did not have to be considered, because in service her weights changed very little. The weight of her slaves being live load, did not strain and press a vessel as would a deadweight cargo. This class of ships could always be kept in proper trim. Their voyages were comparatively short in duration and their ability to keep at sea for a long time was, unlike that of the privateer, of little importance. Because of this, she did not have to carry a large supply of provisions, nor guns and munitions that had much weight. These factors permitted builders to trim displacement down to a minimum and to ballast their vessels properly when fitted out. The ballast, being lower, aided sail carrying power and stability.

Large ships, however, could not be used in the slave trade, after active measures were taken for its suppression. Slaves in large enough numbers to form a complete cargo for a large vessel were rarely found in one place and the time required to gather up a sufficient cargo made it expensive and impractical. A large ship also attracted the unwelcomed attention of naval cruisers; was difficult to hide and required a large crew. In consequence, slaving brigs and schooners were rarely over 110 feet long on deck, or 300 tons burthen, English measurement. Some, of course, were very small, mere pilot boats, or similar vessels. The favorite length for slavers appears to have been from 75 to 100 feet between perpendiculars. The majority of the slaving prizes taken by the Royal Navy fell within these limits.

In this trade the decks became clear, houses and hatches became smaller, and were fewer in number. As there was no necessity for many openings below for slaves, this was natural. The crew and officers appear to have lived largely on deck, as little was done to give them quarters below. Clear, unencumbered decks were handy in managing the vessels so no deck erections appear to have been in use.

These clipper brigs and schooners, like the privateers, were very wet in a seaway. Because of their light displacement, great proportion of ballast, weight of spars, and sharpness, they were not buoyant, in spite of the fact they had no weight of battery to carry. Their freeboard remained low, with bulwarks reduced in height, all of which did not aid in keeping the decks clear of water in blowing weather. In this connection it is worth noting that the pilot boat model privateers usually carried far less number of guns than they were pierced for. When captured by the Royal Navy and their batteries filled out, as a rule they became miserably wet. By reducing their batteries, this fault could be overcome, but with the slavers, this relief was not to be had, hence few slavers were taken into naval service after being captured.

When the American government begun to take an active interest in the trade, they kept watch of the Baltimore ship-builders and inquired into the uses to which the vessels were to be put. The Royal Navy also kept an eye on the Bermudas and on Jamaica, as well as watching the movements of fast sailing craft in the West Indies. This interfered with the Baltimore builders somewhat and many migrated to Havana, Cuba, Brazil, and Central America, and for a short time built vessels for the slave trade in these places. This building, of course, died out with the trade.

The majority of the vessels employed in the slave trade, between 1820 and 1850, appear to have been built in the United States, Cuba, and Brazil. Very few were built in Europe, or in Africa. None that became notorious in the trade appear to have been built in the British West Indian Colonies after about 1828.

The crews were usually rather large and were naturally an adventurous lot. The officers were often a reckless, hard drinking and fighting outfit, and the most of them were cruel and brutal. Some, in spite of their character, were good sailors and officers. The fast, Baltimore-built heeler, whose decks they graced, was made to travel. A brig slaver, 105 feet on deck, carried 40 men in her crew in 1831, which was in proportion to slaver practice. A man-of-war brig of 100 feet would have had 75 to 100 men.

The rigs used in the slave trade were but two, generally speaking, the brig and schooner, the preference being for the brig rig. Very few appear to have been brigantines. There were a few sloops, mostly Brazilian, and a very few full-rigged ships, late in the history of the trade. The preference for the brig was probably due to the fact that the slaver operated generally in open water, and that the square rig was best suited for deep-sea voyaging. Very few fore-and-aft schooners were used; practically all of them were either topsail schooners or brig schooners. A few small fore-and-aft schooners of the shallow, pilot boat type were employed as tenders on the African coast, and a few were used to lighter slaves in the West Indies. The slaver proper generally sported yards. Even the Brazilian sloops, built on Bermuda-sloop model, carried square sails.

The average slaver, schooner, or brig, was around eighty feet in length on deck, but the small size did not prevent their carrying very large cargoes. Judging from lithographs and paintings of captured slavers, there appears to have been little difference in the appearance of slaver brigs. All had the same straight sheer, deep, short head, rather low freeboard and all were heavily sparred. The schooners show a great deal more variation, both in hull and rig. Some have heads, some not; the proportions of spars seem to vary quite a bit, provided, of course, these prints were correctly drawn.

Before studying an actual slave brig, there are a few plans of Baltimore Clippers of 1820 to be inspected. These are redrawn from Marestier's book, "Memoire sur les bateaux a vapeur des Etats-Unis d'Amerique," by M. Marestier, Ingenieur de la Marine Royale, Chevalier de le Legion d'Honneur; printed in 1824, in Paris. This is a report in two volumes on the steamships built in the United States, with descriptions, calculations, and drawings. This engineer not only inspected the steamships, machine shops, rope walks, etc., but he also studied the American schooners and apparently the American Navy. The report on the navy unfortunately, however, was never published. The short chapter on schooners gives a mass of information on the vessels of 1812 to 1820, both Baltimore Clippers and pilot schooners. The data, while incomplete on some of the vessels, is highly useful. This chapter, or as Marestier heads it "Appendice," describes the data thus, freely translated:

THE AMERICAN SCHOONERS

"The schooners of the United States are so often praised in the French Navy that I have accordingly procured plans of some of them.

"I present, in two plates, the plans of eight vessels of this type, which are published in order that the lines generally used in them can be made known, but in order to judge better, in a general way, the proportion usually followed by the Americans, I not only report on the principal dimensions of the eight shown in the plans, but also those of ten others of various sizes. I have classified them according to their length.*

No. 1.   The Mammouth† [Mammoth]

	Dimensions		Proportions to length	to beam
Length	35.05 m.	[114′ - 11$\frac{11}{16}$″]	1	4
Beam	8.76	[28′ - 8$\frac{13}{16}$″]	0.25	1
Draft forward	3.05	[10′ - 0$\frac{1}{16}$″]	0.087	0.348
Draft Aft	4.88	[16′ - 0$\frac{3}{32}$″]	0.139	0.557

"This vessel is now rigged as a brig, and armed as a privateer under the name *Independence of the South* [*Southern Independence?*]. She carries 16 guns. Formerly she was rigged as a schooner, and was called the *Mammoth*. This name was given her, it is said, because she was the largest schooner built until then. There have been larger schooners constructed since, but usually they are soon rigged as brigs.

---

* The data is given by Marestier in the metric system and the proportions of length and beam to other elements may be easily calculated on this basis. The principal dimensions have been reduced to feet and inches for ready reference. These are placed in brackets alongside the metric dimensions. The notes on each ship are translated from Marestier. (1 meter = 3.2803 feet or 39.37 inches.)

† Built during the War of 1812.

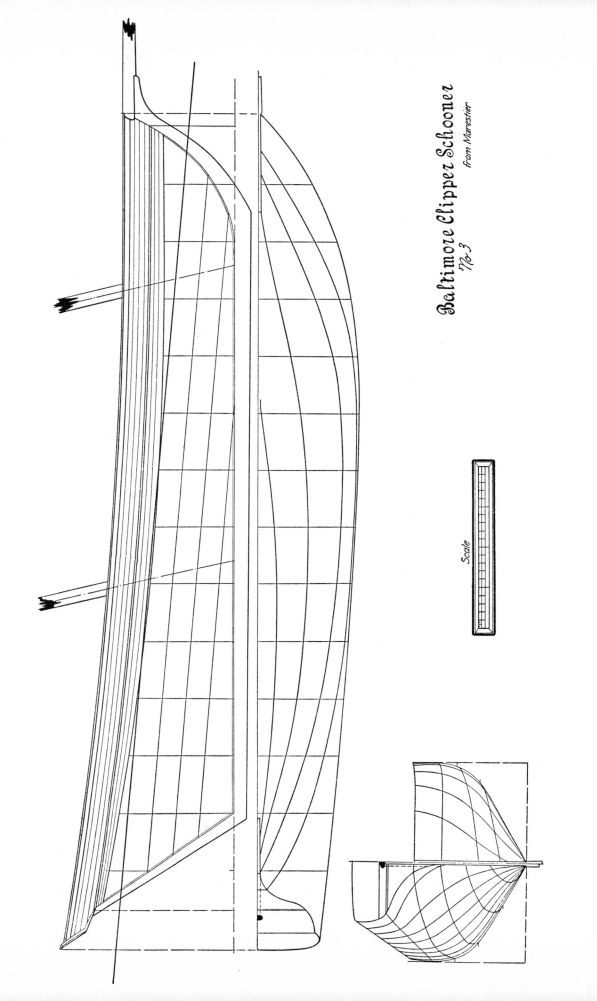

Baltimore Clipper Schooner
No 3
from Marestier

Scale

No. 2.

		Dimensions	Proportions to length	to beam
Length	32.20 m.	[105' - 7½"]	I	4
Beam	8.05	[26' - 4⅞"]	0.25	I
Depth at midsection	3.96	[13' - 1³⁄₃₂"]	0.123	0.492
Length of mainmast	25.6	[83' - 11²³⁄₃₂"]		3.18
Length of foremast	25.0	[82' - 0³⁄₃₂"]		
Diameter of mainmast	0.53	[1' - 8²⁷⁄₃₂"]	0.021 of the length	
Diameter of foremast	0.58	[1' - 10²⁷⁄₃₂"]		

No. 3.

		Dimensions	Proportions to length	to beam
Length	31.33 m.	[102' - 9¼"]	I	3.956
Beam	7.92	[25' - 11¾"]	0.253	I
Depth at bow	3.35	[10' - 11⅞"]	0.107	0.423
Depth at midsection	3.63	[12' - 0³⁄₃₂"]	0.115	0.458
Depth at stern	5.47	[18' - 0¹⁄₃₂"]	0.175	0.691
Overhang of stern	5.45	[17' - 11¼"]	0.174	0.688
Distance midsection is for'd of center	4.13	[13' - 6⁹⁄₁₆"]	0.132	0.521
Rake of sternpost	3.87	[12' - 8¹¹⁄₃₂"]	0.124	0.489
Spacing of frames, nearly	0.57	[1' - 10⁷⁄₁₆"]	1/55	0.072
Length of mainmast	25.6	[83' - 11²³⁄₃₂"]		3.232
Length of foremast	25.0	[82' - 0³⁄₃₂"]		
Diameter of mainmast	0.51	[1' - 8³⁄₃₂"]	0.02 of the length	
Diameter of foremast	0.55	[1' - 9²¹⁄₃₂"]		

No. 4.

		Dimensions	Proportions to length	to beam
Length	30.18 m.	[99' - 0"]	I	3.884
Beam	7.77	[25' - 5²⁷⁄₃₂"]	0.257	I
Depth at midsection	4.11	[13' - 5²⁵⁄₃₂"]	0.136	0.529
Length of mainmast	25.0	[82' - 0³⁄₃₂"]		3.218
Length of foremast	24.1	[79' - 0²¹⁄₃₂"]		

"This vessel was designed to be armed for war service.*

No. 5.

		Dimensions	Proportions to length	to beam
Length	29.26 m.	[95' - 11²⁵⁄₃₂"]	I	4
Beam	7.315	[23' - 11¹⁵⁄₁₆"]	0.25	I
Depth at midsection	3.05	[10' - 0¹⁄₁₆"]	0.104	0.417
Length of mainmast	22.55	[73' - 11⅝"]		3.083
Length of foremast	21.80	[71' - 6⅛"]		
Length of bowsprit	8.60	[28' - 2⁹⁄₁₆"]	0.294	1.176

* War of 1812, of course.

CAPTURE OF AMERICAN SLAVER "MARY ADELINE," OFF THE CONGO, IN 1852
BY H.M. BRIGANTINE "DOLPHIN"

From a colored lithograph by H. John Vernon, in the Macpherson Collection

BRITISH PRIZE BRIGANTINE "NETUNA," BEATING OFF THE SPANISH SLAVER "CAROLINE"
MARCH 20, 1826, IN THE BIGHT OF BENIN

The *Netuna* carried 1 gun and 5 men; the *Caroline*, 10 guns and 90 men. From a colored aquatint,
after the painting by W. Joy, in the Macpherson Collection

THE CAPTURE OF THE SLAVER "BOLODORA," BY H.M. SCHOONER "PICKLE," JUNE 6, 1829

From the colored aquatint, after the painting by W. J. Huggins, in the Macpherson Collection

CAPTURE OF THE SPANISH SLAVER "MIDAS," JUNE 27, 1829, ON THE GREAT BAHAMA BANK
BY H.M. SCHOONER "MONKEY"

From the colored aquatint, after the painting by W. J. Huggins, in the Macpherson Collection

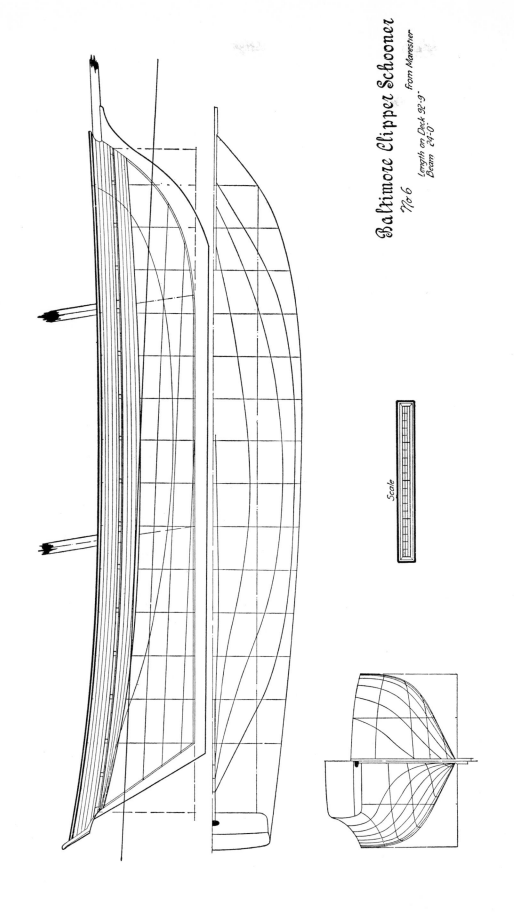

Baltimore Clipper Schooner
N⁰ 6
Length on Deck 92'-9"
Beam 24'-0"
From Marestier

Scale

No. 6.

	Dimensions		Proportions to length	to beam
Length	28.28 m.	[92' - 9$\frac{3}{16}$'']	1	3.863
Beam	7.32	[24' - 0$\frac{1}{8}$'']	0.259	1
Depth of bow	3.37	[11' - 0$\frac{21}{32}$'']	0.119	0.460
Depth of midsection	3.05	[10' - 0'']	0.108	0.417
Depth at stern	4.04	[13' - 3'']	0.143	0.552
Overhang of bow	6.10	[20' - 0$\frac{1}{8}$'']	0.216	0.833
Distance midsection is for'd of center	1.64	[5' - 4$\frac{9}{16}$'']	0.058	0.224
Rake of sternpost	2.97	[9' - 8$\frac{29}{32}$'']	0.105	0.406
Thickness of keel	0.18	[0' - 7$\frac{3}{32}$'']		0.025
Spacing of frames, nearly	0.46	[1' - 6$\frac{1}{8}$'']	1/62	

"The frames are alternately double and single.

Height of floors at middle	0.23	[0' - 9$\frac{1}{16}$'']		0.031
Thickness of floors	0.18	[0' - 7$\frac{3}{32}$'']		0.025
Thickness of lower futtock	0.10	[0' - 3$\frac{15}{16}$'']		0.014
Beams sq. 17 in. no. pine	0.23	[0' - 9$\frac{1}{16}$'']		0.031
Length of mainmast	22.0	[72' - 2'']		3
Length of foremast	21.3	[69' - 10½'']		
Diameter of mainmast	0.43	[1' - 4$\frac{15}{16}$'']	0.02 of its length	
Diameter of foremast	0.46	[1' - 6$\frac{1}{8}$'']		

"I saw this vessel in construction.

No. 7.

	Dimensions		Proportions to length	to beam
Length	27.43 m.	[88' - 9$\frac{7}{8}$'']	1	3.964
Beam	6.92	[22' - 8$\frac{13}{32}$'']	0.252	1
Depth at bow	3.15	[10' - 4'']	0.115	0.455
Depth of midsection	2.75	[9' - 0¼'']	0.100	0.397
Depth of stern	3.92	[12' - 10$\frac{5}{16}$'']	0.143	0.566
Overhang of bow	4.75	[15' - 7'']	0.173	0.686
Distance midsection is for'd of center	2.31	[7' - 6$\frac{15}{16}$'']	0.084	0.334
Rake of sternpost	1.90	[6' - 2$\frac{25}{32}$'']	0.069	0.275
Spacing of frames, early	0.61	[2' - 0$\frac{3}{8}$'']	1/45	

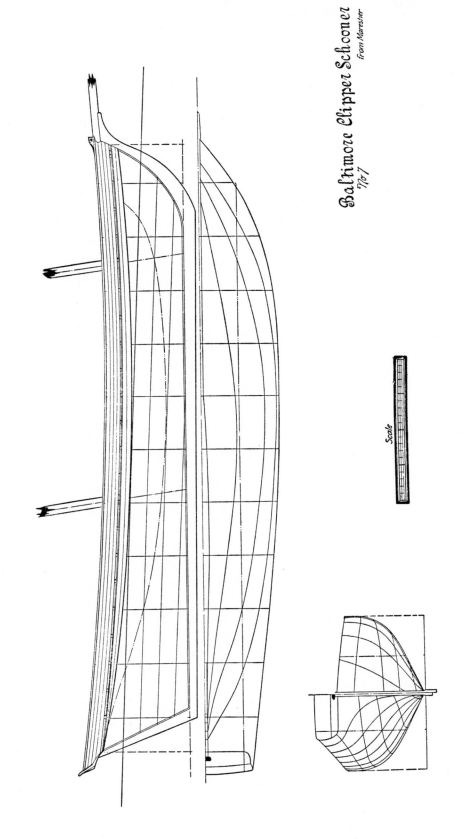

Baltimore Clipper Schooner
No 7
from Marester

Scale

No. 8.

	Dimensions		Proportions to length	to beam
Length	26.0 m.	[86′ - 11⅛″]	1	3.955
Beam	6.70	[21′ - 11¾″]	0.253	1
Depth at bow	2.54	[8′ - 4″]	0.096	0.379
Depth at midsection	2.90	[9′ - 6$\frac{5}{32}$″]	0.109	0.433
Depth at stern	4.42	[14′ - 6″]	0.167	0.660
Overhang of bow	2.75	[9′ - 0¼″]	0.104	0.410
Distance midsection is for'd of center	3.40	[11′ - 1$\frac{27}{32}$″]	0.128	0.507
Rake of sternpost	1.22	[4′ - 0$\frac{1}{32}$″]	0.046	0.182
Spacing of frames, nearly	0.61	[2′ - 0″]	1/43	
Depth of keel at the bow	0.53	[1′ - 3$\frac{5}{32}$″]		
Depth of keel at the stern	0.28	[0′ - 11″]		

No. 9.

	Dimensions		Proportions to length	to beam
Length	23.80 m.	[78′ - 0$\frac{27}{32}$″]	1	3.526
Beam	6.75	[22′ - 1$\frac{23}{32}$″]	0.284	1
Depth at bow	2.87	[9′ - 5″]	0.121	0.425
Depth at midsection	2.78	[9′ - 1$\frac{7}{16}$″]	0.117	0.412
Depth at stern	3.52	[11′ - 6$\frac{1}{16}$″]	0.148	0.521
Overhang of bow	4.67	[15′ - 3$\frac{27}{32}$″]	0.196	0.692
Distance midsection is for'd of center	2.40	[7′ - 10$\frac{15}{32}$″]	0.101	0.356
Rake of sternpost	2.46	[8′ - 0$\frac{27}{32}$″]	0.103	0.364
Spacing of frames, nearly	0.61	[2′ - 0″]	1/39	

No. 10.

	Dimensions		Proportions to length	to beam
Length	23.77 m.	[77′ - 11$\frac{21}{32}$″]	1	3.542
Beam	6.71	[22′ - 0⅛″]	0.282	1
Depth at bow	2.95	[9′ - 9⅛″]	0.214	0.440
Depth at midsection	2.59	[8′ - 6″]	0.109	0.386
Depth at stern	3.40	[11′ - 1$\frac{27}{32}$″]	0.143	0.507
Overhang of bow	4.57	[14′ - 11⅞″]	0.192	0.681
Distance midsection is for'd of center	1.78	[5′ - 10$\frac{1}{16}$″]	0.075	0.265
Rake of sternpost	2.49	[8′ - 2″]	0.105	0.371
Spacing of frames, nearly	0.45	[1′ - 5$\frac{11}{16}$″]	1/52	
Depth of keel at bow	0.30	[0′ - 11$\frac{13}{16}$″]		
Depth of keel at stern	0.30	[0′ - 11$\frac{13}{16}$″]		

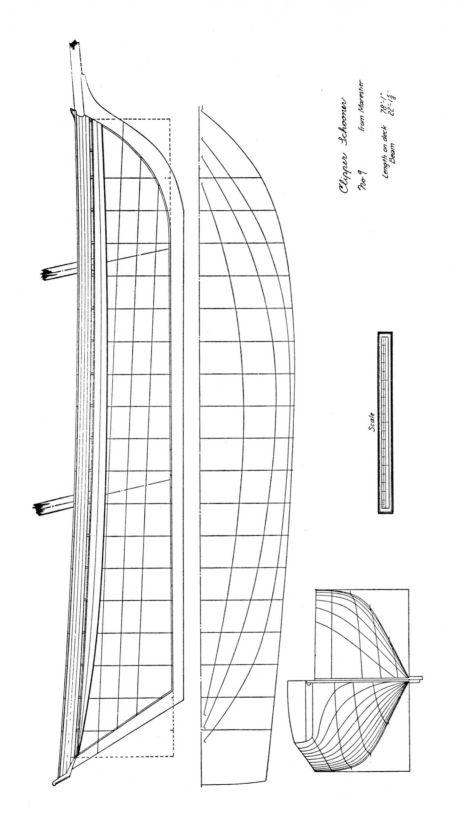

Clipper Schooner
No 9   From Marestier

Length on deck   78'-½"
Beam   22'-5⅜

Scale

No. 11.

	Dimensions		Proportions to length	to beam
Length	23.70 m.	[77' - 8$\frac{29}{32}$'']	1	3.703
Beam	6.40	[20' - 11$\frac{29}{32}$'']	0.270	1
Depth at bow	2.69	[8' - 9$\frac{29}{32}$'']	0.114	0.420
Depth at midsection	2.59	[8' - 6'']	0.109	0.405
Depth at stern	3.51	[11' - 6$\frac{5}{32}$'']	0.148	0.548
Overhang of bow	4.37	[14' - 4'']	0.184	0.683
Distance midsection is for'd of center	2.25	[7' - 4$\frac{9}{16}$'']	0.095	0.352
Rake of sternpost	1.83	[6' - 0$\frac{1}{32}$'']	0.077	0.286
Spacing of frames, nearly	0.61	[2' - 0'']	1/39	

No. 12.

	Dimensions		Proportions to length	to beam
Length	21.95 m.	[72' - 0$\frac{1}{32}$'']	1	3.43
Beam	6.40	[20' - 11$\frac{29}{32}$'']	0.292	1
Depth at bow	2.57	[8' - 5$\frac{5}{32}$'']	0.117	0.402
Depth at midsection	2.50	[8' - 2$\frac{13}{32}$'']	0.114	0.391
Depth at stern	3.20	[10' - 6$\frac{1}{16}$'']	0.146	0.500
Overhang of bow	4.57	[14' - 11$\frac{7}{8}$'']	0.208	0.714
Distance midsection is for'd of center	1.52	[4' - 11$\frac{13}{16}$'']	0.069	0.238
Rake of sternpost	2.17	[7' - 11$\frac{13}{32}$'']	0.099	0.339
Thickness of keel	0.18	[0' - 7$\frac{3}{32}$'']		0.028
Spacing of frames, nearly	0.41	[1' - 4$\frac{5}{32}$'']	1/54	

The frames are alternately single and double.

Height of floors at center	0.23	[0' - 9$\frac{1}{16}$'']		0.036
Thickness of floors	0.15	[0' - 5$\frac{29}{32}$'']		0.023
Thickness of lower futtocks	0.10	[0' - 3$\frac{15}{16}$'']		0.016
Space or room between frames, nearly	0.16	[0' - 7$\frac{5}{16}$'']		0.025

"This vessel was in construction when I saw her.

No. 13.

	Dimensions		Proportions to length	to beam
Length	20.6 m.	[67' - 6$\frac{7}{8}$'']	1	3.377
Beam	6.1	[20' - 0$\frac{3}{32}$'']	0.296	1
Depth of midsection	1.83	[6' - 0'']	0.089	0.300

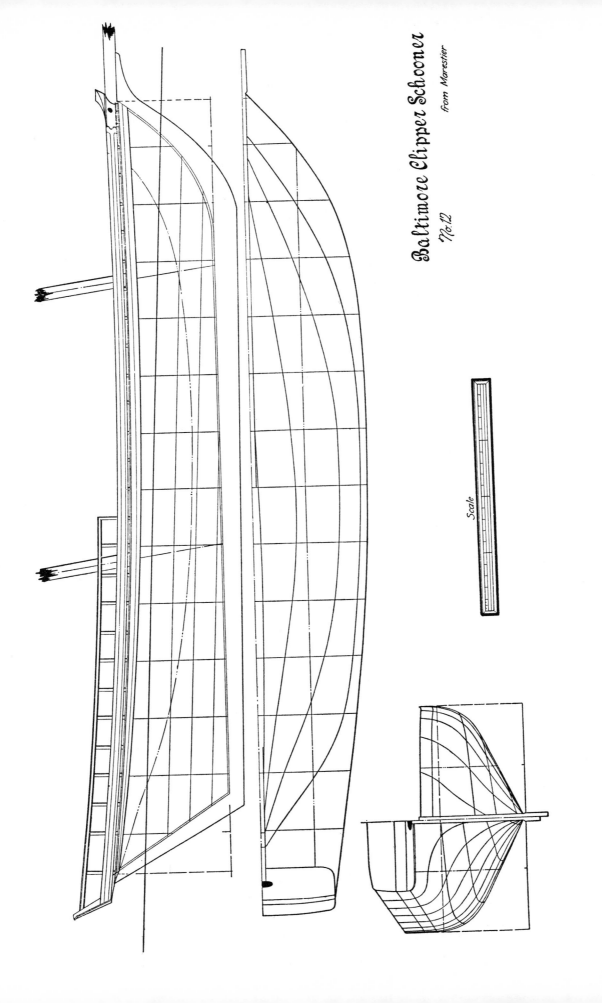

Baltimore Clipper Schooner

No. 12

from Marestier

Scale

No. 14.

Pilot Boat

	Dimensions		Proportions to length	to beam
Length	18.95 m.	[62' - 1$\frac{15}{16}$"]	1	3.452
Beam	5.49	[18' - 0$\frac{3}{32}$"]	2.90	1
Depth of midsection	1.83	[6' - 0$\frac{1}{32}$"]	0.097	0.333
Draft of water at bow	1.22	[14' - 0"]	0.064	0.222
Draft of water at stern	2.13	[6' - 11$\frac{27}{32}$"]	0.112	0.388
Length of mainmast	17.8	[58' - 4$\frac{21}{32}$"]		3.24
Length of foremast	17.2	[56' - 5$\frac{1}{16}$"]		
Diameter of mainmast	0.36	[1' - 2$\frac{5}{32}$"]	0.02 of the length	
Diameter of foremast	0.38	[1' - 2$\frac{15}{16}$"]		

"The masts are without shrouds. The bulwarks do not extend above the deck. This vessel cost $2,213.25. The pilots of the Virginia coast all use vessels of this type. The vessel following is a second example.

No. 15.

	Dimensions		Proportions to length	to beam
Length	18.59 m.	[60' - 11¾"]	1	3.589
Beam	5.18	[16' - 11⅞"]	0.279	1
Depth at midsection	1.98	[6' - 6"]	0.107	0.382
Draft of water for'd	1.22	[4' - 0"]	0.069	0.236
Draft of water aft	2.13	[6' - 11$\frac{27}{32}$"]	0.115	0.411
Depth of keel at bow	0.38	[1' - 2$\frac{15}{16}$"]		
Length of mainmast	17.8	[58' - 4$\frac{21}{32}$"]		3.43
Length of foremast	17.2	[56' - 5$\frac{1}{16}$"]		
Length of bowsprit	4.3	[14' - 1¼"]	0.23	0.83
Length of mainboom	11.0	[36' - 1"]	0.59	2.12
Length of each gaff	3.7	[12' - 1⅝"]	0.20	0.52
Length of maintopmast	5.5	[18' - 0½"]	0.30	1.06
Diameter of mainmast	0.34	[1' - 1⅜"]	0.02 of its length	
Diameter of foremast	0.37	[1' - 2$\frac{9}{16}$"]		

"The sails are fourteen cloths at the foot and five at the head. The masts are without shrouds. The bulwarks do not extend above the deck. This vessel cost $2,164.30.

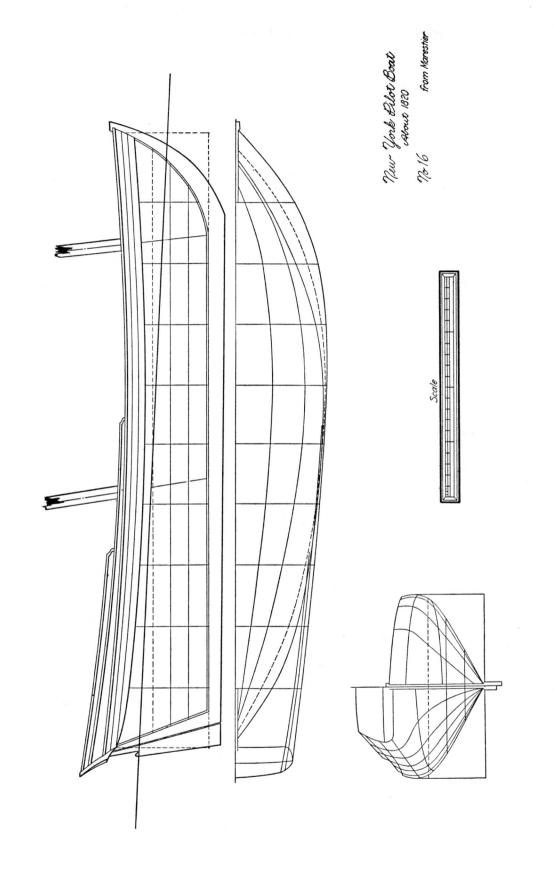

New York Pilot Boat
About 1820
No 16

from Marestier

Scale

No. 16.
Pilot Boat

	Dimensions		Proportions to length	to beam
Length	17.96 m.	[58' - 11"]	I	3.367
Beam	5.35	[17' - 6½²⁄₃²"]	0.298	I
Depth at bow	2.40	[7' - 10¹⁵⁄₃₂"]	0.134	0.449
Depth at midsection	2.09	[6' - 10¼"]	0.116	0.391
Depth at stern	2.70	[8' - 10⁹⁄₃₂"]	0.150	0.505
Overhang of bow	3.35	[10' - 11²⁷⁄₃₂"]	0.187	0.626
Distance midsection is for'd of center	1.66	[5' - 5¹¹⁄₃₂"]	0.092	0.310
Rake of sternpost	1.02	[3' - 11¼"]	0.057	0.191
Spacing of frames, about	0.45	[1' - 5²³⁄₃₂"]	1/40	

"This plan is that of a New York pilot boat.

No. 17.

	Dimensions		Proportions to length	to beam
Length	17.45 m.	[57' - 2⅞"]	I	3.144
Beam	5.55	[18' - 2¹⁵⁄₃₂"]	0.318	I
Depth at bow	2.13	[6' - 11²⁷⁄₃₂"]	0.122	0.384
Depth at midsection	1.83	[6' - 0¹⁄₃₂"]	0.105	0.330
Depth at stern	2.36	[7' - 8⅞"]	0.135	0.425
Overhang of bow	3.05	[12' - 0³⁄₃₂"]	0.175	0.550
Distance midsection is for'd of center	1.68	[5' - 6⅛"]	0.096	0.303
Rake of sternpost	1.84	[6' - 0¹³⁄₃₂"]	0.105	0.332
Spacing of frames, nearly	0.46	[1' - 6³⁄₃₂"]	1/38	
Length of mainmast	18.3	[60' - 0¹¹⁄₃₂"]		3.30
Length of foremast	17.7	[58' - 0²³⁄₃₂"]		
Diameter of mainmast	0.37	[1' - 2⁹⁄₁₆"]	0.02 of its length	
Diameter of foremast	0.38	[1' - 2¹⁵⁄₁₆"]		

"This plan, I was told, is that of a pilot boat from Virginia, though the difference of draught of water is very much less than that in schooners No. 14 and No. 15.

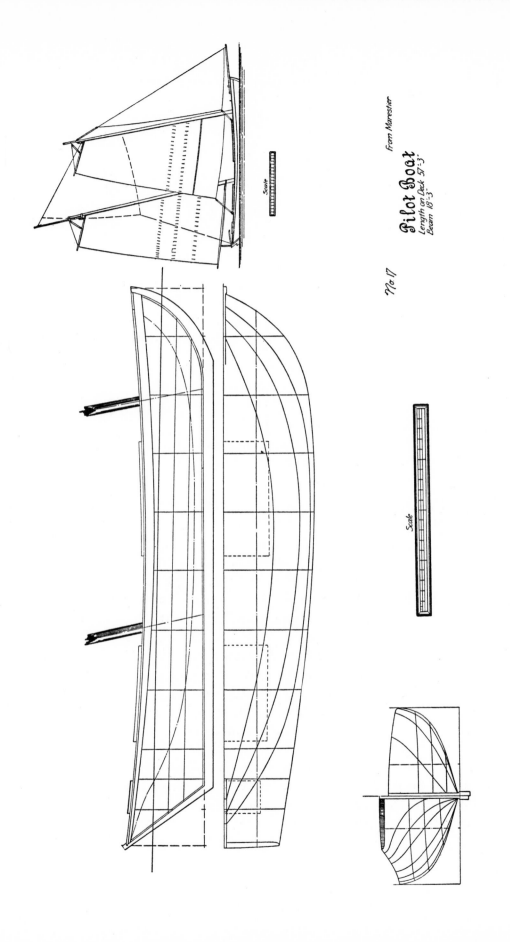

From Marestier

No 17

Pilot Boat
Length on Deck 57'·3"
Beam 18'·3"

Scale

Scale

No. 18.

	Dimensions		Proportions to length	to beam
Length	16.60 m.	[54' - 5$\frac{7}{16}$"]	1	3.217
Beam	5.16	[16' - 11$\frac{1}{8}$"]	0.311	1
Depth at bow	1.63	[5' - 4$\frac{5}{32}$"]	0.982	0.316
Depth at midsection	1.83	[6' - 0$\frac{1}{32}$"]	0.110	0.355
Depth at stern	3.05	[10' - 0$\frac{1}{16}$"]	0.184	0.591
Overhang of bow	2.90	[9' - 6$\frac{1}{8}$"]	0.175	0.562
Distance midsection is for'd of center	3.12	[10' - 2$\frac{13}{16}$"]	0.188	0.605
Rake of sternpost	1.07	[5' - 6$\frac{15}{16}$"]	0.064	0.207
Spacing of frames, nearly	0.38	[1' - 3"]	1/44	
Length of mainmast	17.4	[57' - 1"]		3.37
Length of foremast	16.8	[55' - 1$\frac{9}{32}$"]		
Length of bowsprit	3.4	[11' - 1$\frac{13}{16}$"]	0.205	0.66
Length of two top-masts each	4.9	[16' - 0$\frac{7}{8}$"]		0.95
Length of mainboom	10.4	[34' - 1$\frac{3}{8}$"]	0.627	2
Length of two gaffs, each	4.0	[13' - 1$\frac{7}{16}$"]	0.241	0.78
Length of lower yard	10.4	[34' - 1$\frac{3}{8}$"]	0.627	2
Length of topsail yard	5.2	[16' - 11$\frac{15}{32}$"]	0.313	1
Length of jibboom beyond bowsprit	3.0	[9' - 10$\frac{1}{16}$"]	0.181	0.58
Diameter of mainmast	0.34	[1' - 1$\frac{3}{8}$"]	0.02 of its length	
Diameter of foremast	0.36	[1' - 2$\frac{5}{32}$"]		
Heads of lower masts	1.39	[4' - 6$\frac{11}{16}$"]	1/12 of its length	

"This vessel was to be used in the Revenue Service.

"It will be noticed that the beam of the larger schooners is very nearly a quarter or 0.25 of their length, but from the information just listed, it will be seen that the small schooners and pilot boats had beams usually running over 0.31 of their length.

"The depth of the mid-section does not restrict itself to so narrow a comparison, it often varies from 0.087 to 0.136 of the length, or from 0.300 to 0.529 of the beam, but ordinarily it falls with 0.10 or 0.11 of the length.

"The depth at the bow generally differs little from the mid-section, it is sometimes much less, but in most it is more. The depth* at the stern is not far removed from 0.14 to 0.15 of the length or from 0.5 to 0.6 of the beam.

"The difference of draught of water, fore and aft, is commonly very great, although it is somewhat equalized by making the keel deeper at the bow than at the stern, below the rabbet.

"The overhang of the bow, or rake of stem post, and the rake of the stern

* These depths are depth of vessel from deck to rabbet, apparently.

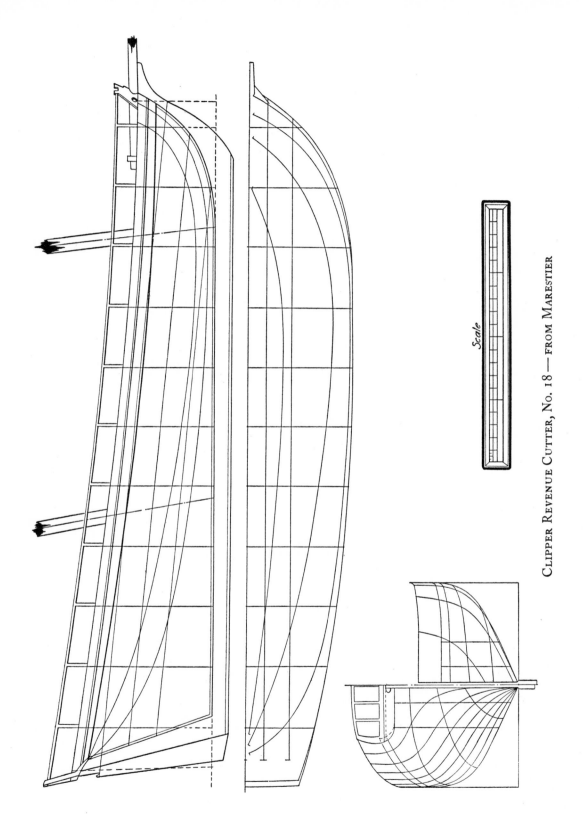

Scale

CLIPPER REVENUE CUTTER, No. 18 — FROM MARESTIER

post, in these vessels, is always great. The rake of the stem post varies from 0.4 to 0.8 of the beam, and the rake of the stern post from 0.2 to 0.4 or even more. The rake of the stem compared to the length is in the proportion of

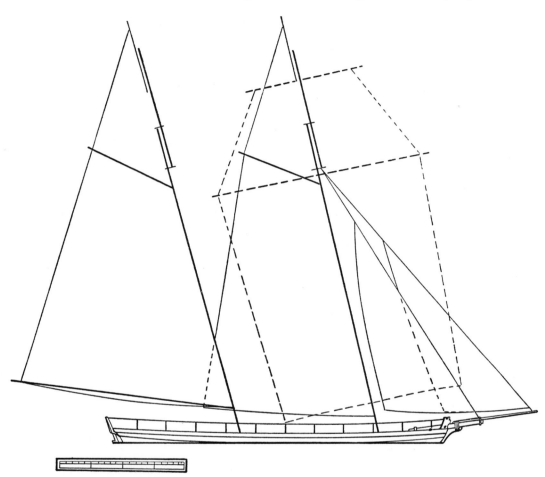

FIG. 22 — CLIPPER REVENUE CUTTER, No. 18 — FROM MARESTIER
Length on deck, 54′ 6″—Beam, 16′ 11″ — Mainmast, 57′ 1″ — Foremast, 55′ 1″

0.1 to 0.2, but it is more often nearer 0.2 than 0.1. The rake of the stern post is usually equal to nearly 0.1 of the length, sometimes, however, it is very near to 0.05. It is necessary to add that when the rake of the stem is reduced, the rake of the stern post is also less.

"The mid-section is rather arbitrarily placed, in that it is usually some distance forward of the beam. This distance varies from 0.058 to 0.188 of the length or from 0.224 to 0.605 of the beam.

"The number of frames which season in place in the vessel is from 38 to

CAPTURE OF THE SLAVER "EL ALMIRANTE," FEBRUARY 1, 1829, IN THE BIGHT OF BENIN
BY H.M. BRIG "BLACK JOKE"

From a colored aquatint, after the painting by W. J. Huggins, in the Macpherson Collection

BRIG "MARY PAULINE" OF SALEM, MASS., FORMERLY THE SLAVER "LALA ROOKH"

Built at Hartford, Conn., in 1833. From the painting in the Peabody Museum, Salem

CAPTURE OF THE SPANISH SLAVER "FORMIDABLE," DECEMBER 7, 1834, OFF SIERRA LEONE
BY H.M. BRIG "BUZZARD"

From a colored aquatint, after the painting by W. J. Huggins, in the Macpherson Collection

CAPTURE OF THE SLAVER "BORBOLETA," MAY 26, 1845, BY THE BOATS OF H.M. BRIG
"PANTALOON," AFTER A TWO DAYS' CHASE OFF LAGOS, WEST AFRICA

From a colored lithograph, after a drawing by H. John Vernon, in the Macpherson Collection

62. The variation shown in this number is probably due to the fact that when all the frames are double they are very widely spaced, and when not more than half or a third are doubled, they are much more closely spaced.

"The mainmast is most commonly placed from 0.45 meters to 0.60 meters, according to the length of the boat, aft of the middle of the rabbet of the keel; and the foremast is placed from 0.15 meters to 0.20 meters aft of the intersection of the rabbet of the stern and keel. The rake of the masts is 15 centimeters per meter according to some builders; others make it about 22½ centimeters. The foremast usually has one or two centimeters less rake than the mainmast.

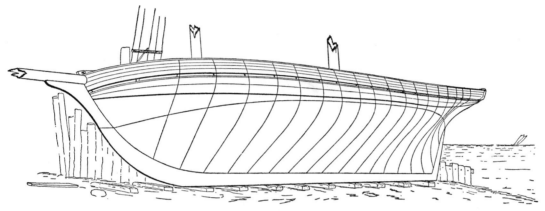

FIG. 23 — BALTIMORE CLIPPER SCHOONER. A PERSPECTIVE PROJECTION

"To find the length of the mainmast, three times the beam of the vessel is added to half the depth. Sometimes the whole depth is added. The diameter of the mainmast is very nearly equal to one-fiftieth of its length.

"The foremast is always from 0.6 meters to 0.9 meters shorter than the mainmast, nevertheless its diameter is from 2 to 4 centimeters greater than that of the mainmast.

"It should be kept in mind, that, in giving these various proportions, I have not presented them as being deserving of absolute confidence as rules of construction. It was not my intention to give the rules of construction of the American builders, rules that are not rigorously observed, as can be observed by study of the eight plans of the schooners. No. 3, 6, 7, 9, 12, 16, 17 and 18, which will aid one to judge better than by proportions. We are less able to rule on the extremes of depth, rake of stem post, rake of stern post, etc. This I have concluded from the comparison of the plans or dimensions given herewith, because it is probable that these extremes would have to be less narrow if the number of vessels was greater.

"The rig of the American schooners was always remarkable for its lightness. In order to show this better I have given three drawings of three different vessels. One schooner carries a topsail forward only. The foremast

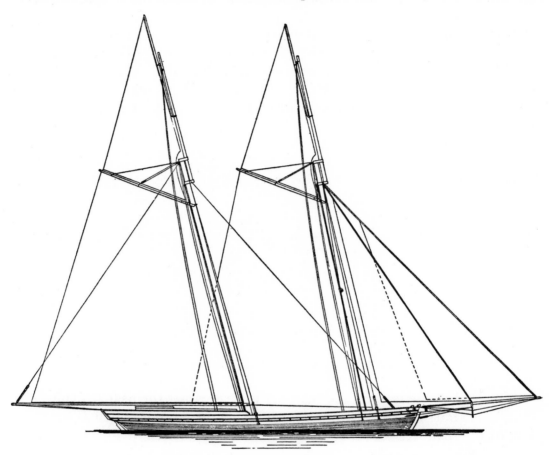

FIG. 24 — BALTIMORE CLIPPER SCHOONER — SAIL PLAN
From Marestier

has three shrouds on a side, and the mainmast has but two. The foresail is sheeted to a boom at the foot. The second schooner does not have a boomed foresail, the topsail yard can be brought on deck. The lower masts each have two shrouds on a side. The third schooner does not carry a square topsail, but gunter fore and aft topsails on both fore- and mainmasts. There is but one shroud to a side on the main and only two on the foremast."

This is the end of the report on the American schooners, the few paragraphs remaining make reference to the common sloops, and also to a centerboard sloop with raking mast. Marestier also states that the three plans of rigging are not to exact scale, being drawn without measurements, giving, therefore, only an idea of the rig of these craft—not exact proportions.

From these data, particularly the proportions, the design of Baltimore Clippers can be studied in detail.

Marestier does not give the degree of deadrise of his examples, but the eight plans that he gives show the wide variation in this respect. This report by a naval architect and technician, is of utmost value as from it a general idea of the proportions for masting can be calculated. The tendency shown in the measurements was toward masts equal in length to the length of deck, in most schooners; the smaller ones had longer spars in proportion. Marestier's notes on proportions of length, depth, rake, etc., need little addition. A careful study of this list of dimensions of eighteen schooners is of great value, as it should be remembered that this report was intended to enable the French naval architects to build counterparts of the Baltimore Clippers, therefore Marestier gives the proportions of beam to length, etc., for all items. Marestier later became one of the French Navy constructors or designers.

The eight vessels shown in Marestier's plates show the Baltimore Clipper as built between 1814 and 1820, the last half of the War of 1812, perhaps, to the early twenties. These vessels, therefore, show the types employed both as privateers and slavers. It will be noted, also, that the pilot boats are fully described.

The plans of Marestier's reports are worth taking up in detail, as there are many points worthy of particular attention.

The pilot boats are perhaps the most interesting. Number 17, for example, is the type of pilot boat employed at the entrance to Chesapeake Bay. Unfortunately the transom was not shown in Marestier's plan, and in redrawing it, the transom was reconstructed from other data, as was the sail plan. This reconstruction is from the old painting of a "Virginia Pilot-Boat with a distant view of Cape Henry." The vessel is practically a double ender, with a stern almost like a bugeye's "Patent Stern," but built into the hull. The form is rather easy and the lines are fuller forward than the deeper pilot boats. The low freeboard is particularly noticeable in this example. Like others of her type she has no bulwarks. This is probably the type of vessel used as a 1-gun privateer such as was frequently sent out of the southern ports during the early part of the War of 1812. They seem to have had a large hatch, amidships; another hatch or a low house just aft of the mainmast; and a small cockpit or helmsman's hatch right aft against the stern post. They steered with a tiller, of course. The name and port of the vessel was usually carried about half way up the foresail, which had a little more area than the mainsail. These vessels must have been able to handle and sail under foresail alone.

The other pilot boat, Number 16, is the New York type. This also represents the small 1-gun privateer, like that sent out from New York and the northern ports. She is deeper and sharper on the bottom and has bul-

FIG. 25 — BALTIMORE CLIPPER SCHOONER — SAIL PLAN
From Marestier

warks. The waterline indicated is a reconstruction and is approximate only. The raising of the stern is unusual, though otherwise she differs a little from the extreme type of Baltimore Clipper. Her transom probably extended outboard of her planking at the rail, as in the *Flying Fish*, and the other privateers and Baltimore schooners that have been discussed. Her transom is a reconstruction.

Number 18 is an extreme type; her beam runs very far forward, and her freeboard is extremely low, if the waterline indicated is intended for a load waterline. Her open rail is of the type that is very common on the Chesapeake Bay, even yet. The general design is somewhat along the *Grecian's* lines but not so fine. Her deadwood forward is more marked. The rig is reconstructed from the dimensions given, and is approximate only. The stern

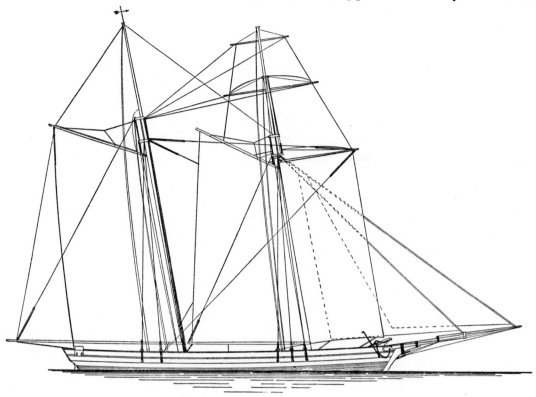

Baltimore Clipper Schooner
Sail Plan
FIGURE 26—FROM MARESTIER

is short, and probably her transom was similar to the *Flying Fish*, in extending beyond the planking at the rail. This transom is also reconstructed in this plan.

Number 3 is the only one having a flat transom or square tuck. She has less beam in proportion to her length than most of the type. She seems to be very large for the type of stern indicated. This is the only vessel in Marestier's plans having the square tuck. All the others show the cant timber aft for the round tuck stern. Number 3 is a very handsome schooner, nevertheless, and is quite sharp. She shows a raking mid-section and has the earmarks of having been a fast vessel. She would have been a good vessel for the slave trade, though larger than most schooners in the business.

Number 9 is a schooner that has lines very similar to the two-masted schooners built in the Bahamas for the fruit trade, thirty years ago. The rake of the ends and shape of the mid-section are very like those of these Bahama schooners, and she is about the same size. The amount of beam differs little, also. These Bahama schooners were very fast, some are still afloat, and judging from this, Number 9 must have had a good turn of speed.

Number 6 is a lovely schooner, with a graceful sheer and well-shaped cutwater and head. Her transom is like that of the New York pilot boat, and is also reconstructed in this drawing. She is very sharp and has a little more freeboard than the others. This one seems to be the best-lined vessel in Marestier's plans.

Number 12 is a merchant schooner, no doubt; perhaps a Chesapeake Bay trader. Marestier saw her building, but does not state what she was designed for. She has, as can be seen, an open rail, but it does not run the length of the deck. She has a longer head than any of those given in the plans.

Number 7 is another sharp schooner with more sheer than is usual in the type. The rake of the ends is not so great as some of those described. She has a very easy run. This is another fast vessel.

Any of these vessels could have been used as privateers or slavers. They all show that the Baltimore builder understood how to design a fast vessel. These eight schooners not only represent the highest development of the type, as in Number 6, but also the decadent tendency that had begun to show after the War of 1812, as may be noted in Number 18, the revenue vessel. This desire for fast vessels had begun to lead the builders to extremes in deadrise and draft, combined with low freeboard, long spars, and a large proportion of displacement in ballast. It is doubtful if Number 18 would be as fast a vessel in all around sailing as the others, but she evidently was designed for some particular service where such sailing qualities as she had could be used to the best advantage.

Vessels such as these represented in the eight plans of Marestier, were in use in the West Indies and along the American coast as traders, slavers, pirates, and revenue cutters or naval cruisers, until about 1830, when the type became generally speaking, much more extreme. As has been said, the development of vessels in the slave trade was, no doubt, directly responsible for the change.

Plans of slave vessels are difficult to find. The type was unsuited, usually, for naval service, so when captured they were either sold as prizes, to private parties, or destroyed. The few that were in naval service were generally used as tenders. Fewer still had their lines taken off. Basil Lubbock has found one, the brig-schooner *Fair Rosamond*, a Baltimore-built schooner, and the writer found a brig, the *Diligente*, through the efforts of Mr. C. Knight, the Admiralty Curator. Mr. Lubbock will probably publish the plans of *Fair Rosamond* shortly. She is not so extreme as the *Diligente*.

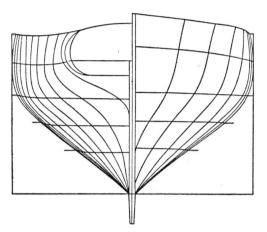

FIG. 27—LINES OF SLAVE BRIG "DILIGENTE"

The plan of *Diligente* shows the most extreme type of Baltimore Clipper. Nothing is known as to her place of building; it was probably Baltimore or Havana, Cuba. A curious feature in her lines was discovered when redrawing this plan, namely, that her draft of water, load waterline to rabbet, is greater forward than aft, by a few inches, and yet her draft, to bottom of keel, is just the opposite as she draws more water at the stern. Apparently she was intended to float with the rabbet level and went slightly by the head. Her dimensions are not given on the original draught, nor is her tonnage. The draught scales 100 feet between perpendiculars, 26 feet extreme beam, and depth of hold about 14 feet. The original draught was rather ragged and torn, but the lines were in good shape and very clear.

The plan has the following title: "Dimensions of Masts and Spars of Slave Brig *Diligente*. Note, Scale ¼ to a foot. Benj. C. Oakshott. Bermuda. Nov. 12th, 1839." This is all that the plan has to say, and shows only her lines, deck plan and spar dimensions. The original drawing was not complete, the body plan showed only the transom and nine sections. In redrawing the rest of the sections were faired in.

This vessel has the extreme elements of design that marked the last of the Baltimore Clipper models. Her deadrise is very great, her bilges, hard, and her waterlines are sharp. The most marked development in her body plan is the slight hollow in the deadrise, particularly from amidships forward. Her ends are much shorter than the pilot boat models of earlier years. The rake of the ends is not so excessive and this may be because of her rig. Her keel is deeper aft than forward. This last is directly opposite to what Marestier found to be the prevailing custom twenty years earlier, when he mentions the fact that the keels were commonly deeper at the bow. Her waterlines are very sharp for the period, particularly at the bow. The run is long, straight and lean, as was always common in the Baltimore Clippers. The sheer is very slight, a feature very common in American vessels until the fifties. The cutwater and head are short and deep, with a billet and scroll, probably in white or gold. The bow has more curve than most Baltimore vessels; this is also probably due to her rig. The stern has a short overhang and the transom, like the most of Marestier's schooners, extends beyond the planking at the sides. The rudder is very narrow and deep. The plan does not show whether she steered with a tiller or wheel, but probably the latter.

The load waterline was indicated on the original draught by two faint pencil lines. This was probably her sailing trim. Her freeboard is very low. The bulwarks, about 3½ feet high, help out somewhat, but she must have been fearfully wet when under a press of sail in a strong breeze. Her lines are given to the outside of the planking, quite an unusual feature in old plans.

The deck plan is marked by its lack of openings and deck erections. The greatest beam is well forward, and the top of rail has a hard turn at the third station aft of the bow perpendicular. Her greatest beam is about eight feet forward of amidship, but the beam on the rail is carried much further forward. She has a low trunk cabin top or house, right aft; a small hatch just forward of this; and the usual double pump wells forward of the hatch. These are octagon, in section, instead of round or square. The mainmast comes next, with a large hatch opening into the slave decks, between it and the foremast. Forward of the foremast is a riding bitt and forecastle hatch. There is a smaller bitt at the heel of the bowsprit. No galley is shown, but it was probably either on deck, West Indian fashion, or in the forecastle. She was probably painted black.

The masts have a great amount of rake and the bowsprit a fair amount of steve. The sail plan is drawn from the spar dimensions given on the draught. Sail plans of slavers are extremely rare and spar dimensions are marked by their absence. Therefore, as an additional factor in studying this vessel's sail plan, her spar dimensions are given herewith. As preliminary notes of points of interest, the reader's attention is called to the fact that the foretopmast, 'gallant mast, skysail pole, foreyard, topsail, gallant and royal yards are exactly the same as the corresponding spars on the main. The only difference is in the length of the lower and royal masts, otherwise the spars are interchangeable. She does not appear to have had the trysail mast common in man-of-war brigs.

MASTS AND YARD DIMENSIONS OF "DILIGENTE"

	Main		Fore	
	Length	*Diam.*	*Length*	*Diam.*
Mast, whole length	60' - 0"	19½"	58' - 5"	19½"
Head	9' - 9"		9' - 9"	
Topmast	34' - 5"	10½"	35' - 5"	10½"
Head	5' - 5"		5' - 5"	
Gallant mast, heel to stop	18' - 6"		18' - 6"	
Royal	11' - 0"	7½"	10' - 0"	7½"
Skysail	6' - 6"		6' - 6"	
Yard, Main	57' - 0"	12¾"	57' - 0"	12¾"
Topsail	42' - 6"	9½"	42' - 6"	9½"
Gallant	25' - 0"	5 "	25' - 0"	5 "
Royal	14' - 7"	4 "	14' - 7"	4 "
Bowsprit, whole length	31' - 0"	19½"		
Jibboom, whole length	38' - 3"	10½"		
Jibboom, Flying length	35' - 7"	7"		
Main Boom	53' - 0"	11½"		
Main Gaff	36' - 4"	8¾"		
Swinging Booms	33' - 0"	6½"		

This rig, with its extreme dimensions, shows very well the trend of the Baltimore type. The lower yards are greater in length than half the deck length. The head spars are tremendous for this size craft and must have made the *Diligente* pitch heavily. The whole design is marked by extreme dimensions and it is doubtful if the type ever became more extreme. This vessel, we may feel certain, represents the final development of Baltimore Clippers.

It is unfortunate that nothing is known, at present, of the history of the *Diligente*. Sired by War, mothered by Privateering and Piracy, and nursed by Cruelty, nevertheless, the Baltimore Clipper will always remain the type representative of the highest development of small sailing craft, as built by American builders. The vessels, represented by the *Diligente*, were able to evade the Royal Navy cruisers, and later, the Americans, for many years. It was not until the market for slaves was finally closed that slaving ceased. While the horrors of "the Middle Passage," and the vicious cruelty and bestiality of the slavers has placed a blot on the Baltimore Clipper of the '30's, yet the daring of the American builders in producing so extreme a class is much to be admired. It must be said, however, that the builders of slavers resorted to highly unprincipled actions in order to get their vessels into the slave trader's hands. Shanghied crews, bribed officials, and murder were not uncommon; and as most of the Baltimore Clippers built for the slave

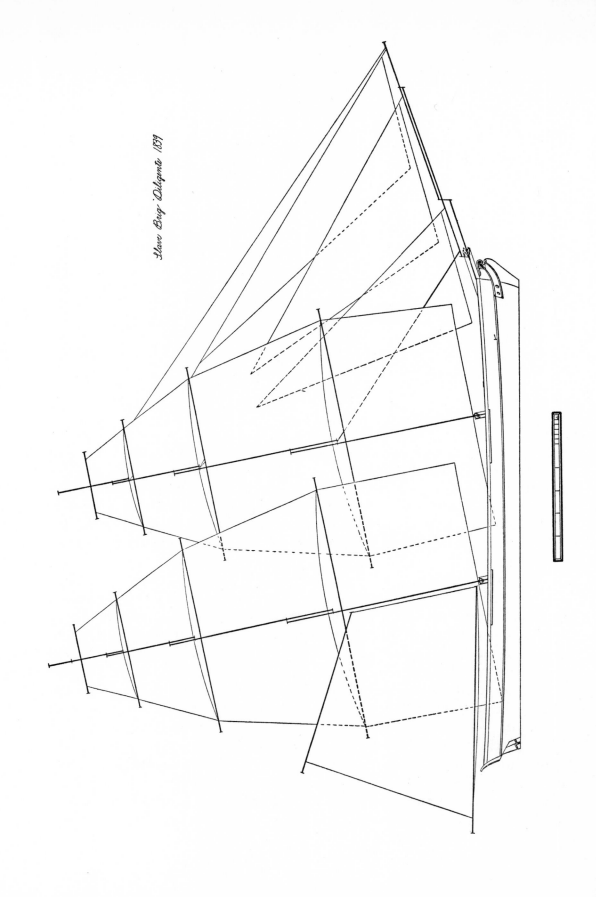

Slave Brig 'Diligente' 1839

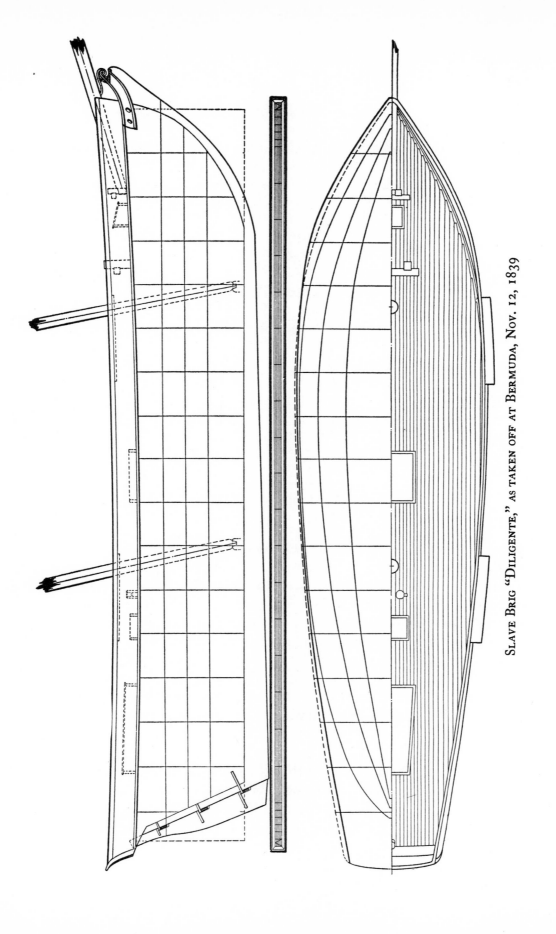

Slave Brig "Diligente," as taken off at Bermuda, Nov. 12, 1839

trade were built on speculation, it follows that these builders were, usually, the guilty parties, as well as the owners.

The American Government, toward the end of the trade, kept a watchful

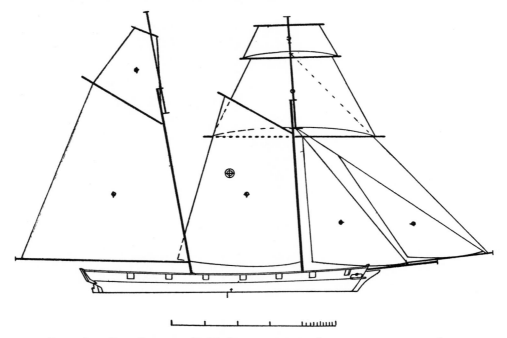

FIG. 28 — SAIL PLAN OF R. N. SCHOONER OF 182 TONS, OF ABOUT 1831, PROBABLY H. M. S. "SPIDER"

eye on the yards of ship-builders who were known to be favored with orders for slavers or who could finance the building of a heeler on speculation. When it was discovered that a vessel was being fitted for the trade, all kinds of red tape and all sorts of obstacles were put in the way of the owners or builders to prevent or discourage them from fulfilling their intentions. This end was not usually achieved, and many a fast brig and schooner entered the trade, eventually either to founder or to fall a victim to Royal Navy cruisers, hidden reefs, fire, or a slaves' mutiny. A few were cut out and destroyed by the negroes on the African coast and some were destroyed through accidents in the West Indies. The number of slave ships lost appears to have been very great, throughout the life of the trade, though there are, of course, no complete records.

It was during the slave trade that the many light sails, seen later in clipper ships, first appeared. In the slave brigs, particularly, the rig was added to in the form of queer and numerous light sails. Studding sails outside of studding sails were said to have been used by slavers, as well as water sails, ringtails, gunter skysails, moonrakers, etc. Starting with the same rig as the man-of-war brig, the slaver captain was not satisfied until he had a complete suit of light sails for ghosting weather. Whenever he could set a sail, he proceeded to do so, cutting out all kinds of oddities, as a result. This practice was followed, particularly in the Royal Navy, by the cruising man-of-war brigs on the African coast. The rigs of gun brigs in this service were increased and the brigantine rig was often employed in these vessels in preference to the regular brig rig. Slavers do not seem to have employed the rig quite so much, though a number had the spar plan, no doubt.

After the War of 1812, there were a large number of slaver schooners crossing the Atlantic, but during the '30's and '40's these schooners were used largely as tenders in procuring slaves on the African coast and their place in the Atlantic trade was taken by larger brigs. However, schooners were employed up to the very end. The New York Yacht Club schooner *Wanderer*, is a well-known example.

The slave trade, indirectly, was the cause of the disappearance of the Baltimore Clipper, as a type. Not only had the type become marked by such extremes that they could not be used for general trade, but their very appearance at sea caused mariners to have fears and suspicions, due to their torrid past and usual employment. With the passing of this terrible trade the star of the Baltimore type settled and disappeared.

CHAPTER VI

THE END OF THE BALTIMORE CLIPPER

THE cessation in building the Baltimore Clipper type was not sudden nor can any date be placed upon it. The disappearance of the type was gradual and was marked by revivals, but nevertheless few of the type were left by 1860.

Toward the end of the history of this type we find a few clipper ships that were built on regular Baltimore Clipper lines. The *Architect* and *Ann McKim* were ship-rigged Baltimore Clippers, both merely enlarged schooner hulls. The *Ann McKim* was built in 1832, at Baltimore, for Isaac McKim, by Kennard and Williamson, of Fells Point, and was named in honor of the owner's wife. She was ordered built on schooner-clipper lines. According to Clark, she was 493 tons register, length 143 feet, breadth 31 feet, depth 14 feet, drew 17 feet aft and 11 feet forward. She had very raking masts. Her frames were live oak and she had mahogany hatch coamings, companionways, skylights, rails, stairs and trim. She carried twelve brass guns, and brass capstan heads, bells, etc. She was a three-skysail yarder and had royal studding sails. In spite of her small cargo capacity she was her owner's pet ship, as she was very fast. She sailed in the China trade, until 1837, under the McKim flag, and until 1847 under the Howland and Aspinwall flag. She ended her career under the Chilian flag. She was a very beautiful ship. Fortunately, Hall's report on "The Shipbuilding Industry of the United States" gives her lines which are redrawn here. These lines are probably fairly accurate and represent the vessel within a couple of inches. The original drawing in Hall's book is rather a poor piece of engraving.

These lines show the great amount of deadrise that this vessel possessed, the rake of her ends and generally sharp lines that we have seen in smaller vessels of the type. The transom is flat and there is no counter. This vessel is another example of the extreme in deadrise and draft that the type reached in its last development. In regard to the drawing of this ship—her bow shows a billet head, but her registration papers state she had a woman's bust as a figurehead. She became hogged during her career, due to her light construction. She was said to be one of the fastest vessels built at Baltimore; her

TOPSAIL SCHOONER "LOUISA," OF CHARLESTON, SOUTH CAROLINA

From the painting by Antoine Roux, 1826, owned by M. Alp. Cyprien Fabre

AMERICAN TOPSAIL SCHOONER

From a lithograph after a drawing by P. le Comte in "Afbeeldingen van Schepen en Vaartuigen,"

Amsterdam, 1831

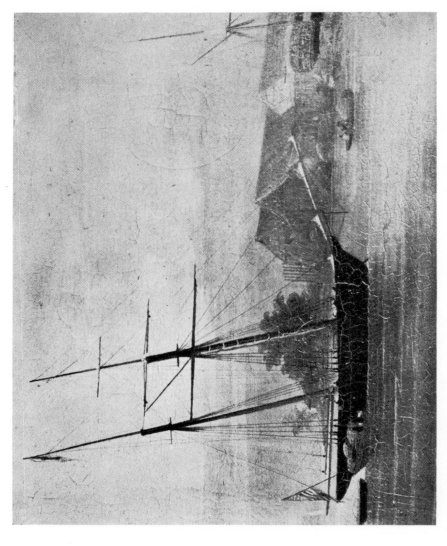

SCHOONER "BRENDA," 31 TONS, BUILT AT BOSTON, IN 1845
Used in the Chinese opium trade. From an oil painting in the Peabody Museum, Salem

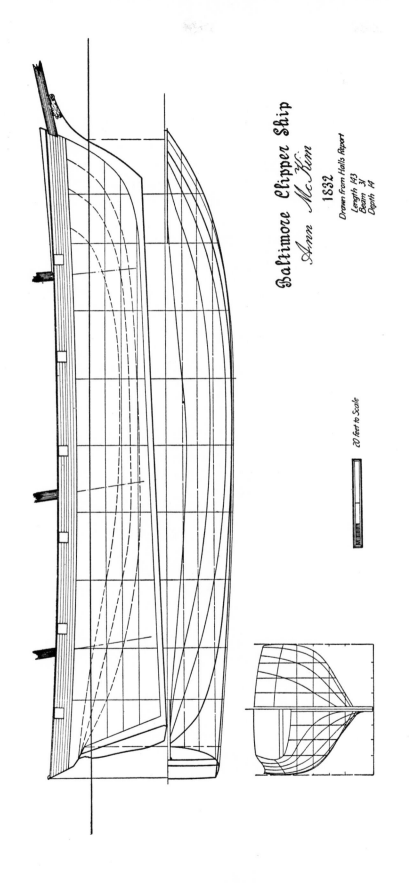

Baltimore Clipper Ship

Ann McKim

1832

Drawn from Halls Report

Length 143
Beam 31
Depth 14

20 feet to Scale

rival was a famous brig, the *John Gilpin*. A complete set of plans appeared in the "Rhode Island Mariner," in 1927 and 1928, from which some of this data is taken. A comparison of this vessel with the *Hannibal* is interesting in showing the development in the ideas of Baltimore ship-builders, in the design of square-rigged ships, in the twenty-two years that intervened between the building of these ships. The *Ann McKim* was the first extreme clipper ship ever built, but she did not start the clipper ship era, nor was her model repeated, apparently. Her draft and lack of carrying capacity prevented this, no doubt. However, she was owned by Howland and Aspinwall, and these shipowners built the *Rainbow*, in 1843, the first extreme clipper ship of the fleet constructed during what is known as the "Clipper Ship Era." So, perhaps, the *Ann McKim* was the forerunner of this famous fleet.

Another Baltimore Clipper ship that had a turn of speed was the *Architect*, 520 tons, built near Baltimore, in 1847, for the China trade. This vessel made some rapid passages to China, but little is known of her. Whether or not she was as extreme in form as the *Ann McKim* is a matter of conjecture; probably not, as she was evidently more of a carrier, though not much larger.

These vessels were really the last development of the Baltimore Clippers in the direction of increase in size, but in the *Ann McKim*, for example, there was no change in form. None of the type had cargo space, and now, with thirty or more years of peace, the necessity of speed at all costs was removed. Shipowners were now building larger and larger ships, and demanded greater cargo carrying capacity in proportion to tonnage than had been the practice in earlier years. Furthermore, the Baltimore Clipper type was impractical to construct in vessels of over 600 tons, as the draft, if built to the regular Baltimore model, would be much too great, and the capacity only that of a freight carrier of half its size. The North Atlantic trade had become of great importance since the War of 1812, and had developed large ships capable of good speed in the type of sailing for which they were designed. The California trade and the gold rush increased the demand for larger ships and greater speed. Since it was found to be impractical to build extremely large Baltimore Clippers, the builders developed the North Atlantic packet, and using this model as a basis, with additional ideas formed from a study of the Baltimore Clippers, they developed the well-known clipper ship.

The Baltimore model, having reached its limit, the ship designers began to experiment with other models and finally the great American naval architect Griffiths evolved the general type of ships illustrated in the American Clipper ships of the '50's. These vessels were of comparatively little deadrise, rather wall-sided, but had long, sharp and hollow bows as well as very long graceful runs. They were powerful ships, able to carry an immense amount of sail and a large amount of cargo in proportion to their tonnage. This last feature was developed to a high point during the existence of the clipper ship. This is just the point in which the Baltimore Clipper model was handicapped, and the natural result was that very few of the latter type were built. The clipper ship, when compared with the Baltimore Clipper, was probably not as fast under general conditions, but due to the clipper ship's greater power, she could make long voyages in shorter time, because she could carry her sail longer in heavy weather and also because she was larger. Undoubtedly in light weather, or to windward in moderate weather, the Baltimore Clipper could outsail the crack clipper ships, but in Cape Horn weather the clipper ship was supreme. No Baltimore Clipper ever built was the equal of *Sea Witch, Challenge, Celestial, Flying Cloud, Young America, Comet, Sword Fish,* and others of the same class under these conditions, but the Baltimore heelers were far their superior in the tropic trades, in light and moderate weather.

While the Baltimore Clipper did not develop into the clipper ship, their forms having little in common, nevertheless through the '40's and early '50's the Baltimore model was employed in the tropic trades, as fruiters, island traders and such, and in the less respectable trades such as the opium trade, and in smuggling and filibustering. These vessels, usually schooners and brigs, were nearly always extreme examples of the Baltimore model and though built at Boston, Portsmouth, or New York, were marked by the same features to be seen in the pilot boat privateers of 1812 and in the later slavers. Throughout the '50's and, in fact, up to the early '70's, some of this class were employed in the West Indies and in the South Pacific island trade.

The opium trade employed a small number of American-built clippers, schooners and brigs, including, also, a bark and a ship or two, but usually the vessels were small pilot boat schooners. The American builders furnished the trade with six schooners, two brigs, and one bark. The English had one ship, and a number of schooners and brigs. Their schooners were developments of the Baltimore Clipper model, usually with less rake to the ends and less drag to the keel. These were fine, yacht-like vessels with raking masts and heavy spars. They carried guns and large crews, to repulse attacks by Chinese mandarin boats and pirates.

The American schooners were the *Anglona*, a 90- or 100 ton schooner built by Brown and Bell at New York in 1841; the 90- or 100-ton schooner *Ariel*, built at Medford, Mass., in 1841, by Sprague and James; the 150-ton schooner *Zephyr*, built by Samuel Hall, at Boston, in 1842; the *Mazep-*

pa, 175-ton schooner, built by Samuel Hall and launched in 1841; and the 300-ton sister schooners, *Minna* and *Brenda*, launched in 1851 and 1852 at Portsmouth, N. H., by George Raynes.

The *Ariel* distinguished herself by capsizing during a trial trip. Built from designs of Joseph Lee, of Boston, by Sprague and James, for Captain Forbes, she was designed to beat the pilot boat schooner *Anglona*, from Brown and Bell's yard at New York. The *Anglona* was used as a dispatch boat at Canton, by Russell and Co. Mr. Lee had designed the *Rose*, a fast brig, and was disappointed that he had not had a chance to design the *Anglona*, so Forbes agreed to take a half interest in the *Ariel*, provided she could beat the *Anglona*. The *Ariel*, as described by Captain Forbes, was a long, low, topsail schooner with very long hard pine masts, and her foremast was stepped very far forward. The hold was so shallow that an ordinary man could stand on the keelson and look over the coamings of the main hatch. Her first trial showing her to be crank, more ballast was added and she was tried again in a strong breeze and capsized without loss of life in the outer bay, Boston harbor. After she was raised, her spars were cut down, and she was sailed to China where she beat the *Anglona* in a course around the Island of Lintin, starting at Macao Roads, a distance of forty miles, for $1,000 stakes.

The proportions of these schooners varied from the Boston pilot schooners of this date. One of the latter, built in 1842, was 66 feet 6 inches in length; 6 feet 9 inches in depth, with a draught of 6 feet forward and 8 feet aft. Her beam was 17 feet 2 inches. Her foremast was 65 feet long and her mainmast 67 feet. She was built by Samuel Hall at East Boston. This craft could not be said to represent the American opium schooners, as most of the latter were apparently quite extreme. It seems reasonable to believe that they were a combination of the elements of the extreme Baltimore Clippers of the '30's with the shoal pilot schooners common around New York and Boston, during the same period.

This last remark is at variance with an earlier statement, that New York pilot schooners were very deep. This needs explanation and from evidence at hand it would appear that pilot schooners built at New York and Boston were much deeper in proportion, in 1818, than they were in 1840. Sometime in the '30's there seems to have been a general reversion to the shoal type of pilot schooner, which lasted into the 1860's. The well-known pilot schooner *Mary Taylor*, designed by Steers, of yacht *America* fame, is an example. A comparison of the *Mary Taylor*, or similar craft of the '40's and '50's, with the New York pilot schooner of Marestier, the pilot boat privateers of 1812, and the Boston pilot schooners of 1825, shows the vessels of the *Mary Taylor* class to be of less proportionate depth. However, there were vessels of the pilot boat type, built about 1840, that were much deeper, particularly around Boston.

The proportions of vessels of this type are best represented in the schooner yacht *Northern Light*, a famous Boston flyer built in 1839, from designs of a clever Dane, Louis Winde (pronounced like the verb "wind"). The designer was well known both for his yachts and his pilot schooners. The *Northern Light* was quite extreme and her dimensions, representing the proportions of small schooners of this period, are of interest. She was 62 feet 6 inches on deck; 47 feet 6 inches on the keel; 17 feet 6 inches beam; 7 feet 3 inches in depth; 8 feet 0 inches rake of stem; 7 feet 0 inches rake of stern post; 1 foot 3 inches sheer; and 2 feet 8 inches deadrise, at half floor. She had a raised quarter-deck. Her spars were long in proportion to her beam; her mainmast was 67 feet long; the foremast was 64 feet long; the rake of the foremast was 2½ inches; rake of the mainmast was 2¾ inches (to the foot); her bowsprit was 16 feet outboard; her main boom was 37 feet long; gaff 18 feet 9 inches; and her fore gaff 18 feet 5 inches. She was registered as 69 90/95 tons. This vessel had lines similar in appearance to Marestier's New York pilot schooner.

In looking over plans of old schooners, and some old brigs, it cannot but strike the observer that nearly all of them were developed from the Baltimore idea. The fast vessels for thirty years after the eclipse of the Baltimore Clipper as a type had the same elements of design in greater or less degree. Fast keel yacht schooners, fruiters, West Indian turtle schooners, fishermen, and even Nova Scotia fishing schooners, show the influence of the Baltimore builders for many years, in fact until very recent times.

The remarks of Griffiths, in relation to the Baltimore Clippers, are few in number, they had become out of fashion when he wrote his books. He stated that they were no longer popular as they drew too much water for coastwise navigation; and since the slave trade was closed there was little employment for such a type; moreover, they had little cargo capacity; and finally, that schooners of less deadrise and more capacity, could be built that would be as fast or faster. This is one of his rather doubtful statements, as he probably had the larger vessels in mind, or centerboards.

In spite of the fact that the type was going out of fashion, in the last of the '40's and through the '50's, the lessons learned in building them were not thrown aside. The pilot schooners, Gloucester fishermen, coastwise schooners, and small trading schooners and brigs, all had the characteristics of the Baltimore type and continued to have them until recent times, as has been said of other classes.

The pilot schooners varied little from the parent type until after 1860, and the fruit schooners, running to the West Indies and Central and South America, were nearly of the same class. Coastwise traders and freighters built on the Baltimore model after 1830 were few in number; some, however, were employed as packets and mail vessels, particularly in the South.

The Gloucester fishermen employed a number of Baltimore-built schooners on the Banks about 1860. These were moderate Baltimore Clipper type and were not successful on the Banks, being too wet. An example in the United States National Museum, at Washington, name unknown, was 61 feet overall, 18 feet beam, and drew 7 feet 6 inches aft. She had a curved stem, sharp entrance, some drag to the keel, medium amount of sheer, and though her stem was both curved and raking, her stern post was nearly vertical—a later departure at Baltimore.

Centerboards were introduced on the Chesapeake very early, say around 1815, and many small schooners were built on modified clipper lines with a centerboard. These vessels were not of the Baltimore Clipper type and an example in the United States National Museum, the *C. Chase*, built in 1846, is of interest in showing the divergence in the local type that had begun to overshadow the famous Baltimore Clippers of wartime vintage. The *Chase* had a rather full, rounding entrance, curved and raking stem, rather flat floor and round, easy bilge. Her run was long and easy finished off with a light, shoal, square stern. Her drag was slight and her sheer rather straight; her length was 60 feet, beam 20 feet, depth of hold 5 feet 3 inches and she was about 60 tons, old measurement.

Vessels of this class had replaced the shoal-keel Bay schooners, by 1850, and very soon thereafter Baltimore and Chesapeake types became shoal centerboarders. A single type of keel vessel remained in use on the Chesapeake and its tributaries for some time—the Chesapeake pungy. This was a direct descendant of the Baltimore Clipper, except that most of them had a sharp stern, like a bugeye. Some had square sterns and these were marked by the extreme hollow lines of their run. Their sterns were wide and flat, and this, combined with their extreme run, made them appear rather odd, when seen from the stern. A few are still afloat. This class is the last that had a design like that of the pilot-boat-built schooners of 1812.

There is a fine model of one in the United States National Museum, the *W. F. McKewen*, built in 1865. The catalogue description is good and is about as follows: "A carvel-built, wooden-keel vessel with moderately sharp, flaring bow, curved strongly, raking stem, long head, sharp floor, long lean run, shallow square stern, raking stern-post, flush deck, lograil except aft of the main rigging where there is an open quarter rail . . . schooner-rig.

New York Pilot Schooner "Gypsey"

From a lithograph in the Macpherson Collection, after a painting by C. Drew

BRIG "WATER WITCH," OF BOSTON, 167 TONS, BUILT AT SCITUATE, IN 1831

From a water color by Francesco Lengi, showing the vessel leaving the Mole of Malaga in 1833

TOPSAIL SCHOONER "H. H. COLE," OF SALEM, 98 TONS, BUILT AT
BALTIMORE, IN 1843

From a painting by Clement Drew, in the Peabody Museum, Salem

Length over all 68 feet; beams 20 feet 9 inches; depth 7 feet." Except for the long head and shallow stern, this vessel is similar to some of Marestier's. The pungy had the reputation of being very fast.

The bugeye had little or no relationship to the Baltimore Clipper. It is believed that they were developed from log canoes. Some were keel boats, but centerboards were more generally used. Most of these craft had no rake to the stem and a moderate rake to the stern post with little drag to the keel. They, like the pungies, had very long graceful heads like that of a Mediterranean galley of 1690. The introduction of this very long head is recent, apparently, and did not come from the Baltimore Clipper, as these either had no head at all or only a short gammon-knee head, with very few exceptions. Apparently the older bugeyes and canoes either were without heads or had rather short ones; but sometime in the '60's, or a little earlier, long heads became very popular.

Just when the pungy replaced the Baltimore Clipper type is a matter of speculation. Pungies were in use in 1847, perhaps earlier. It is possible that these pungies were of the same type as No. 12 of Marestier's schooners. This vessel is very like a square sterned pungy, in profile, it being noted that she had a longer head than the others. If this represents a pungy, then the type was a true Baltimore Clipper, and was not a descendant. The sharp stern on the pungy was used in the smaller craft and probably came from the bugeye or canoe. The craft of the Chesapeake are worthy of very careful research. There can be no doubt but that a lengthy research would add greatly to our knowledge of the history and design of the Baltimore Clipper. A search for half models probably would develop the greatest amount of authentic information.

The employment of Chesapeake schooners on the Banks fishery has been referred to. From the reports of the Fishery Commission it seems that the vessels were of the pungy type and a very few were centerboarders. It is also stated that they were all very fast in moderate weather, but unseaworthy, wet, and most uncomfortable in a blow. This checks up with the remarks of Royal Navy officers in regard to captured American privateer schooners after 1812, and their wetness, in particular, seems to have been the worst fault of the Baltimore Clipper throughout its existence as a type.

Before leaving Chesapeake schooners there is another model in the United States National Museum, of a craft named the *Sunny South*, built in 1855 for the Bay trade and oyster business. She is a keel vessel with sharp bow, slightly raking stem, long head, rising floor, long easy run, wide, square stem, moderate sheer and long, low quarter-deck. The length overall is 75 feet; beam 22 feet; depth of hold 5 feet; 80 tons, old measurement. She was 71 feet between perpendiculars and probably this represents her length on deck. This is a pungy, no doubt.

The fruit schooners and trading brigs and schooners are well represented in the Watercraft Collection in the United States National Museum. These were all fast vessels and most of them were built on Baltimore lines. The brigs were extreme, as were some of the schooners. One of the models is a contract model of a Baltimore builder, presented by John N. Cushing of Newburyport, Mass. This is a brig, 112 feet long, overall; 26 feet 8 inches, moulded beam; 12 feet moulded depth; and 255 tons, old measurement. She is of the type of 1845, and has a sharp bow with almost straight waterlines, high rising floor, slack bilge, long, lean run, heavy, square stern, little sheer, greatest beam on deck, about 1/3 the length from stem. Stem and stern posts have much rake and she has a short head. This model, a half block, is interesting, and the lines of Fig. 29 are taken from it. She is not as extreme in deadrise as the *Diligente*, but has very good lines. Her mid-section is much rounder and her bilge correspondingly slacker. The ports were probably false, painted ports.

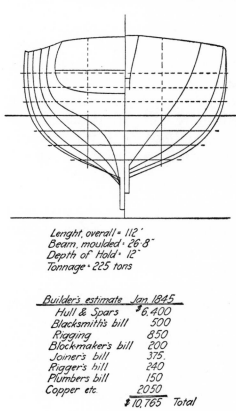

Lenght, overall = 112'
Beam, moulded = 26·8"
Depth of Hold = 12"
Tonnage = 225 tons

Builder's estimate Jan. 1845	
Hull & Spars	$6,400
Blacksmith's bill	500
Rigging	850
Block-maker's bill	200
Joiner's bill	375
Rigger's bill	240
Plumbers bill	150
Copper etc.	2050
	$10,765 Total

FIG. 29 — LINES OF A BALTIMORE CLIPPER-BRIG DESIGNED FOR JOHN CUSHING OF NEWBURYPORT, MASS.

She was to cost $10,765. The model was made in January, 1845, but no vessel was built. John Cushing of Newburyport owned many brigs at this time, usually of the kettle-bottomed type.

There are other models in the National Museum of West Indian trading brigs and all are marked by the features seen in Baltimore Clippers. The models in this museum are worthy of better exhibitions, but due to lack of room, the block models are above the show cases containing rigged models, and are so high that almost nothing can be seen of them. It is to be hoped that eventually these block models will be placed lower so that they can be inspected easily.

It is in the West Indies that we find the Baltimore model lasting longest.

A Draught of a Clipper Brig

Lines taken off builder's half-model, made at Baltimore, Jan. 1845 for John N. Cushing of Newburyport, Mass. Designed for trading on the N.W. Coast of America, but not built. U.S. Nat. Museum N° 76064

While shoal centerboard vessels replaced the clipper on the Chesapeake, the pilot and fishing schooners became affected by yacht styles. Because of his usual isolation, the West Indian held to the old model. Abaco, Harbor Island, and Nassau in the Bahamas; Jamaica, Barbadoes and Grand Cayman; of the English islands; Cuba and Haiti, too, are still building vessels that are modeled on approximate Baltimore lines.

The schooners built at Barbadoes are rigged Ballahou, and are very like the Baltimore Clipper in model. Their foremasts are almost vertical and their main rakes aft. They have no boom on the foresail which overlaps the main and the foregaff has little peak. The jib is large and is cut very full. The mainsail has a lug or gunter gaff, set like a gunter jib topsail which almost parallels the mast. Some apparently have a regular gaff, which, however, is peaked up to an extremely sharp angle. These vessels usually have nearly plumb bows, sharp deadrise, little sheer, short, full transom, square on deck and with a good deal of rake to the stern post. Except for the bows, their model generally follows the clipper model.

A similar schooner was used in England in the pilot service in Bristol Channel in the '60's and '70's. These were the Swansea pilot boats, a snug little schooner of from twenty-five to thirty tons. They had the true Ballahou rig and an English authority described them as follows:

"The rig comprises mainmast, foremast, and running bowsprit; the mainmast is stepped exactly in the middle of the boat and has a great rake aft, so that the head of the mast nearly plumbs the after part of the cockpit. Two sheaves are cut in it through which the halyards are rove. The foremast is upright, with sheaves like the mainmast, and a block on the fore part, under the sheave holes, for the jib halyards. These masts require no rigging or stays, and are pole masts without topmasts. The gaffs are short, for a boat of twenty-five or thirty tons. They are only about six feet long and only require one halyard. One end of the halyard is spliced to a single block, the other being passed over the first sheave in the mast, then through a single block which is hooked to the gaff, and finally through the upper sheave in the mast. This end is belayed. A purchase is formed by a rope passed through the block on the halyard and through a block on deck. The fore halyards are rigged the same way, and the jib halyards are of the ordinary kind. The sails consist of mainmast, foresail, and jib; the two former being laced to the mast. These sails can be taken in in about $1\frac{1}{2}$ minutes and set in about $2\frac{1}{2}$. The outhaul of the jib is passed under a sheave on the stem and acts as a bobstay; there are no shrouds to the bowsprit. The advantages of this rig are said to be that one man can handle a boat of 25 tons himself, and the boats are equally as handy with the foresail as without it, likewise the mainsail. They will stay or do anything either way, and with only the foresail and jib the boat can be sailed on the wind." *

This rig, except for the difference in the running bowsprit and in the main gaff, is very like the Barbadoes schooners, as is the above water profile. Unfortunately we know nothing of the under body of the Swansea boats but probably they were similar to the Barbadoes craft.

This rig has been described at length as the Ballahou was first used in the West Indian Baltimore model schooners. The writer believes that it was adopted to balance the sail plan and hull, as the West India builders began to plumb the stem. These vessels having earned a reputation for speed, the rig was extended to other localities, probably reaching the Bristol Channel through the Royal Navy, which had tenders rigged Ballahou. The Ballahou schooner, it will be remembered, was also known as the Bermuda schooner, in the '30's, though Ballahou is the older name for this rig.

The Bermuda schooner varied in rig. At one period the prevailing rig was Ballahou, at another, both masts raked the same, with very short gaffs, or sometimes leg-of-mutton and also, as we have seen, the favorite Bermuda rig was a three-masted leg-of-mutton schooner, during the early '30's. Unless more data can be had, the rig called Bermuda rig therefore means little. The old "Sailor's Word Book," by Smyth, states that the Ballahou was "A sharp-floored, fast-sailing schooner, with taunt (with much hoist), fore and aft sails and no topsails, common in Bermuda and West Indies. The foremast of a Ballahou rakes forward(?) and the mainmast aft." A similar description has been given earlier, but is repeated for comparing this rig with that of the Swansea pilot boat and the Barbadoes schooner type.

The schooners and sloops of Grand Cayman are also well known in the West Indies. The builders of today are given a good reputation and their boats are fast. While no lines are yet available for close comparison they seem to be strictly on the Baltimore model with very raking ends and much drag and deadrise. Their masts rake aft and they are rather heavily sparred. These vessels are usually small, not over 70 feet overall, as a rule, and are rather handsome. They, like the Bahama schooners, have rather long heads and wide transoms and counters. Some of the smaller have no overhang aft, being finished off with a flat, square transom.

The Bahama craft are numerous and vary widely in proportion and size, and yet they suggest the Baltimore model very strongly. This is not remarkable, as Abaco was settled by Virginians and others from the Chesapeake country, as well as by English and Tory Colonists. The small fishing and sponging schooners of today are keel craft, with raking ends, long heads,

* Dixon Kemp: "Manual of Yacht and Boat Building."

short counter or a flat, square transom, great deadrise and with drag to the keel. Their stems are rounding, and fair into the bottom of the keel well aft of the stem head. Their masts have some rake and they usually have loose-footed sails. Their sheer is often rather great and some are very ugly indeed. The better vessels are nicely modeled and some are handsome craft, though roughly built.

Fifty or so years ago a large number of schooners, of about 60 feet in length, were employed in the deep-sea turtle fishery. These had very raking masts, long and light, with main-topmast only, and single jib. Their ends were very raking; the bow had much curve with a long graceful head. They were keel vessels, of course, and had much deadrise. They had no counter, but a wide, flat transom, quite sharp on the bottom and with a rudder outside. These schooners steered with a tiller, as most small Bahama vessels do. Their freeboard was low, in fact their general appearance was like a square-sterned pungy of the Chesapeake. These schooners have now disappeared, the last, the *President*, going ashore at Gun Cay, in 1926, during the hurricane in September. They were very handsome vessels but during their last days were quite unkempt.

Of the larger types, there are still in existence a few of the Bahama schooners built for the fruit trade. These were about 90 feet long and were fine, able schooners, of the Baltimore design, somewhat modified. An example of their dimensions as taken from a builder's model, having a length, between perpendiculars, of 85 feet; beam, 24 feet; draft at stern, 9 feet; freeboard at stern, 5 feet 3 inches; draft foreward, 6 feet 6 inches; freeboard at boom, 6 feet 8 inches; least freeboard, 4 feet 6 inches; rake of stern post, 1 foot; rake of stern, 10 feet; deadrise, 8 feet from keel, 4 feet amidships. The vessel has six inches of tumble-home in her topsides. She has a graceful head, short, wide counter, flat on the bottom, and her greatest beam is forward of the middle of her waterline length about 1 foot 2 inches.

This vessel shows the general characteristics of the fruit schooner built in the Bahamas from 1860 to 1910, almost without change of model. The older vessels had more drag to the keel and more rake to the ends, but the later built boats could carry more cargo and therefore replaced the old type. After the decadence of the fruit trade, in the Bahamas and West Indies, these vessels became traders and lumber vessels. Some are still active, knocking around the Bahamas or other islands in the British West Indies.

All these types developed in places where the Baltimore Clipper had been built for local purposes and eventually certain changes were made to fit local ideas or needs, and this continued until the original model was almost extinct. Today the type is practically non-existent on the Chesapeake, Bermu-

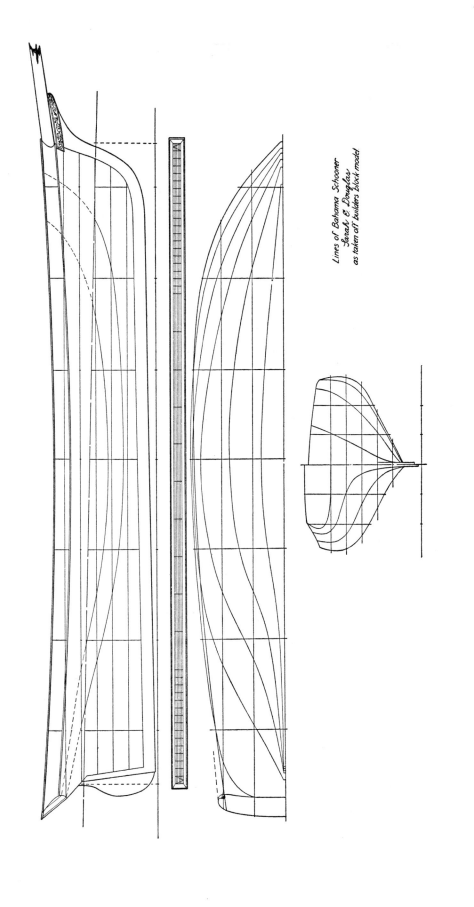

Lines of Bahama Schooner
Sarah E. Douglas
as taken off builders block model

da, and along the mainland, but the model is still more or less followed in
the more remote islands in the West Indies. Vessels having the same appearance as those of Grand Cayman are built on the south coast of Cuba, but
they are not so fast nor are they as well built. Furthermore, they are often
wretchedly kept.

However much influence the Baltimore Clipper had in the type as illustrated in the pilot boat model, the privateers of the 1812 period, and the
rakish slavers of the '30's, it was completely out of fashion before the Civil
War, and in spite of a few that remained afloat after the building of the
class stopped, the type seems to have disappeared from blue water very completely. They were, like modern yacht classes, developed out of existence,
and except for the few scattering plans and models, there is nothing left of
them. It is unsatisfactory to try to trace their influence on small sailing vessels, even in the West Indies, as other influences, since their time, have in
many cases, so changed the local craft that only tattered remnants of the
original fabric remain.

Before closing this account of the Baltimore Clipper it should be said that
research on the type is still very incomplete. The authors who referred to
them in the past were often influenced by fiction and the imaginative writ-
ings of historians and others. The type was exaggerated but not so much as
many writers would have us believe. The spars, for example, were very long,
but like those of the clipper ships, were in proportion. Old paintings or lithographs are generally helpful in picturing the type, yet, for technical details, cannot be trusted. The apparent size of the vessel is usually exaggerated as was the length of her spars and often the size of her guns. Such pictures were usually painted as a sop to the vanity of the captain and officers.

The plans of vessels which we have used in visualizing the development
and decadence of the type, do not represent all that are in existence. No
doubt more will eventually turn up, and like Marestier, a greater number
of examples may change our ideas of what trend of development was in
force during certain periods that have been referred to.

The type has now disappeared, like the clipper ship and with the Baltimore Clipper went much of the romance of the sea. Now-a-days we hear
of square-rigged, and clipper ships; yet the Baltimore Clipper did more for
the country than the square-riggers. The privateers and small men-o-war,
like the *Enterprise*, were most useful vessels. The romance and the notori-
ety of the "rakish topsail schooner" of poetry and fiction, is due directly to
this type. Truly American, in development at least, it aroused the interest of
foreign powers in American ship-building. Not half the interest existed
abroad in the American clipper ship. The Baltimore Clipper also had an in-

direct influence on the American people in many ways. The brutalities practiced aboard these craft, when used in the slave running trade, were a contributing cause that led to the formation of Abolition Societies, with attending changes in political history that brought on the Civil War. Compared with the clipper ships, the life of the Baltimore Clippers was longer, and their achievements and perhaps their influence were of greater importance in the history of the country. The existence of the type covered a turbulent period in American history and when peace became more permanent the type died out. Although not so striking in appearance nor so imposing in size, these small schooners and brigs are far more worthy of sentiment and research than the much advertised clipper ships of the 1850's, so far as American vessels are concerned.

CHAPTER VII

MASTING RULES AND SAIL PLANS

THE history and some of the technical details of the Baltimore Clipper have been more or less covered in the preceding chapters, but there are a number of things that have not yet been mentioned. The data given by Marestier is of great importance, but as he has given only a few rules for masting and but little information on construction, it is necessary to supply more. It must be noted that there has been some reconstruction work done in the accompanying plans, particularly in the sail and deck plans. With the exception of the deck plans of the "Virginia Built Privateer," the "Virginia Pilot Boat," from Knowles, *Dominica* and the *Diligente*, all the deck plans are reconstructed from the inboard profile. For this reason, the width of hatches, bitts, etc., is only approximate, but the fore and aft position is correct, as this is shown in the original draughts.

Another type of Baltimore Clipper, somewhat modified, no doubt, that has not been mentioned, is the American Revenue Cutter. Unfortunately nothing seems to be available on the model of these craft, but a little data of a general nature follows. They were generally topsail schooners; some were double-topsail schooners or brigantines. The following list of Revenue schooners of 1830-1837 has been compiled by Rear-Admiral Elliott Snow, U.S.N., Cons. Corps.

Name	Tonnage	Notes
Morris		Square topsails forward
Old Dexter	90	Square topsails forward
Portsmouth		Square topsails forward
Pulaski	106	Double topsails
Richard Rush		Square topsails forward
Sam Patch		Square topsails forward
Search		Square topsails forward
South Carolina		Square topsails forward
Swiftsure	116	Square topsails forward
Taney	120	Square topsails forward
Vigilant	100	Square topsails forward
Washington (No. 1)		Double topsails

AN AMERICAN SCHOONER

From a lithograph by N. Currier, published in 1846

HERMAPHRODITE BRIG "GARLAND," OF SALEM, 148 TONS, BUILT AT BALTIMORE, MD., IN 1847. LINES OVER-SHARP TO UNSEAWORTHYNESS; LOST IN A STORM ABOUT 1850

From a water color in the Peabody Museum, Salem

BRIGANTINE "MORNING STAR," 172 TONS, BUILT AT EAST BOSTON, IN 1866
From a lithograph by J. H. Bufford, after a painting by C. Drew

SCHOONER "RIO," 58 TONS, BUILT AT BOSTON, IN 1823
From a drawing in the Peabody Museum, Salem

Name	Tonnage	Notes
Washington (new)	120	Square topsails forward
Woodbury		Square topsails forward
Wolcott	90	Square topsails forward
Wasp		Square topsails forward
Marion	100	Double topsails
Jackson	120	Double topsails

The vessels noted as having double topsails were brig-schooners, often rated as brigantines. Some of these vessels were on Baltimore models, in fact, a great many were built on the Chesapeake. Of the Navy schooners and brigs, the brigs *Perry* and *Bainbridge*, in 1850, and the topsail schooners *Porpoise* and *Dolphin*, represented the Baltimore model as developed and changed for naval needs. These, however, are of little use as examples to the Baltimore type, as they were so greatly modified.

It will be interesting to go further into masting rules. While we have Marestier's notes and proportions, there are still other rules that are worthy of inspection. The best and most authoritative are probably Fincham's. A clever naval constructor in the Royal Navy, he was practicing when the Baltimore Clipper was in use and when some were employed in the Royal Navy. He undoubtedly had a good opportunity to study their rigs and his rules and examples were taken largely from the Baltimore types and may be used today. This is particularly true of the later type of vessels. Using Professor Rankine's notes as a check, Fincham's rules may be applied with fairly accurate results, at least one may be sure that a rig so reconstructed is well proportioned and practical, though the resultant rig is perhaps a little small for American vessels.

Rankine found that the plain sail of nearly all vessels could be approximated by an equivalent triangle. This was drawn over the profile of the vessel. Its base (called base of sail) was equal to the distance from the tack of the jib to the clew of the driver or mainsail. In vessels whose length was between $3\frac{1}{2}$ and 4 times the breadth, the base, in proportion to the waterline length for brigs, was from 1.6 to 1.65 and for schooners 1.6 to 1.7. The middle of the base of sail was found in the majority of cases to be forward of the center of the lateral area of the underbody of the vessel, from .05 to .0625 of the base of sail, for brigs and schooners. The height of the ∇ is equal to three times the height of the center of effort of the sails, above the base of sail, but this is of little importance in determining spar dimensions. The base of sail is a useful check on head spar lengths, as well as to determine the length of main or driver booms. Rankine gives a modification of Fincham's rules for masting schooners as follows:

"A schooner is a fore and aft rigged vessel with two masts, fore and main, or three masts, fore, main, and mizzen. The bowsprit is either a running bowsprit, in one piece, or a small standing bowsprit with a jibboom. Each of the masts has a topmast like that of a cutter. On the lower masts are spread gaff sails like a cutter's mainsail, but in general the aftermast of these alone (main sail when there are two masts, driver when there are three) has a boom. The maintopsail and the mizzen topsail (if any) are gaff topsails; the fore topsail and the foretopgallant sail are usually square, and sometimes there is a square foresail, like that of cutter. A jib topsail may be set on the fore topmast stay, which runs from the foretopmast head to the jib-boom end, and a maintopmast staysail on the main-topmast stay, which runs from the maintopmast head to the cap of the foremast. Sometimes the mainmast has a square sail topsail and topgallant sail."

The following proportions, for two masted schooners, are founded on Fincham's rules and examples:

Base of sail = line of flotation × from 1.6 to 1.7.

Leverage of sail = extreme breadth × about 1.75.

Height of center of effort, above base of sail = extreme breadth × about 1.12.

Area of sail = area of loadwater line section × about 3.6.

Line of flotation = extreme breadth × about 2.7.

Sails set: jib, forestay topsail, foresail, mainsail, square fore-topsail, gaff main-topsail.

Station for masts in fractions of line of flotation from the middle (Line of flotation is length taken at L W L, rabbet to rabbet): mainmast, abaft, .05 to .11; foremast, fore, .28 to .34.

Rake of mainmast aft = from 1 in 6 to 1 in 4.

Rake of foremast aft = from 1 in 10 to 1 in4.

SAILS

Nock of the mainsail above water = extreme breadth × from .2 to 2.4.

Nock of the foresail above water = extreme breadth × from 1.8 to 2.3.

Leech of the main- and foresails = luff × from 1.2 to 1.3.

Inclination of main- and fore-gaffs, 25° to 30° from horizontal.

Clew of mainsail abaft stern post at waterline = line of flotation × from .2 to 2.6.

Foot of mainsail extends from clew to mainmast.

Head of mainsail = foot of mainsail × from .5 to .6.

Foot of foresail = foot of mainsail × from .7 to 8.5.

Head of foresail = head of mainsail × from .75 to 1.0.

Tack of jib fore stem, on load waterline = line of flotation × from .41 to .46.
Foot of jib = line of flotation × from .32 to .35.
Foot of square fore-topsail = line of flotation × from .5 to .6.
Head of square fore-topsail = foot of same × from .6 to .9.
Depth of fore-topsail = extreme beam, nearly.

BOWSPRIT MASTS AND YARDS

Bowsprit, from heel to cap = line of flotation × about .33.
Bowsprit, length outboard = line of flotation × about .12.
Jibboom = line of flotation × about .4.
Steeve of bowsprit = from 1 in 6 to 1.4.
Mainmast, from heel to hound = extreme breadth × from 2.6 to 2.8.
Foremast, from heel to hounds = mainmast × from .9 to .97.
Nock of each gaff sail, below hounds of masts = hounded length × about .045.
Heads of lower masts = topmasts × from .3 to .4.
Head of bowsprit = jibboom × about 1/3.
Topmasts hounded = extreme breadth × from .83 to 1.0.
Pole heads of topmasts = hounded length × about .5.
Main boom = line of flotation × from .66 to .7.
Main gaff = main boom × from .44 to .53.
Fore gaff = main gaff × .73 to 1.00.
Fore yard = line of flotation × from .48 to .57.
Fore-topsail yard = fore yard × from .7 to .75.
Fore-topgallant yard = fore yard × from .42 to .48.
Square sail yard on mainmast, main-topsail yard and main-topgallant yard, are nearly equal to corresponding yards on the foremast.
Square sail boom = line of flotation × from .37 to .44.

In a three-masted schooner, the bowsprit, fore- and mainmasts, with their spars and sails, are of the same dimensions, or nearly so, with those of a two-masted schooner of the same size, except that the sails are sometimes taunter, that is, more deep and lofty, the height of the nock of the mainsail, above the water, being as much as 2.6 times the extreme breadth; but the station of the mainmast is somewhat further forward being .03 of the line of flotation abaft the middle, or thereabouts.

The mizzenmast is about .36 or .37 of the line of flotation, abaft the middle. It rakes aft about 1 in 4 or 5; the rake of the mainmast is made somewhat less.

The height of the nock of the driver, above the waterline, is about .65 of that of the nock of the mainsail.

Length of the mizzenmast, heel to hounds = mainmast × about .75.

Head of mizzenmast = topmast × from .3 to .4.

Mizzen-topmast = main-topsail mast × about .9.

Driver boom = line of flotation × about .4.

Driver gaff = main gaff × about .9.

The three-masted schooner rig spreads a proportionately greater area of sail than any other, being in some examples nearly five times the area of the load water section.

A brig is a two-masted, square-rigged vessel, each of the two masts having course, topsail, topgallant sail, and a royal. There are also skysails (sky scrapers and flying kites). There is a standing bowsprit with a jibboom and flying jibboom.

Besides the square sails and fore and aft sails, on the bowsprit, a brig has also a large gaff mainsail, sometimes called the "driver," and a gaff sail on the foremast, called the "fore trysail." When the driver is bent to rings on a trysail-mast, the brig is called a snow.

The proportions founded on Fincham's rules and examples are:

Base of sail = line of flotation × from 1.6 to 1.65.

Leverage of sail = extreme breadth × height of center of effort, above base of sail = extreme breadth × about 1.1.

Area of sail = area of load water section × from 3.5 to 3.75 = line of flotation × extreme breadth × about 2.8.

Sails set: jib, fore course, fore-topsail, fore-topgallant sail, main course, main-topsail, main-topgallant sail, and driver.

Stations of masts in position of line of flotation from the middle: mainmast abaft, from .14 to .15; foremast, forward, from .31 to .33.

The centers of the square sails are about .05 of the extreme breadth afore the center of the masts on which they set.

Rake of the mainmast, aft = from 1 in 16 to 1 in 13.

Rake of the foremast, aft = from 0 to 1 in 50.

Steeve of bowsprit = from 1 in 3 to 1 in 2.8.

SAILS

Nock of the driver is nearly on a level with, or a little below, the center of effort of the jib courses, driver, topsail and topgallant sails.

Clew of the driver, abaft the stern post, at load waterline = line of flotation × from .16 to .19.

Foot of driver extends from clew to mainmast.

Head of driver = foot × about .6.

Leech of driver = luff × about 1.5.

Tack of jib, fore stem, at load waterline = line of flotation × about .45.

Foot of jib = line of flotation × about .3.

Luff of jib = length of jibstay from fore-topmast head to jibboom end × about .8.

Leech of jib = luff × about .8.

Height of head of main-topsail, above base of sail = height of center of effort above base of sail × .2 nearly.

This height is divided into two nearly equal parts for the main course and main-topsail.

Depth of main-topgallant sail = the same height × from .30 to .34.

Depth of fore course = depth of main course × from .80 to .84.

Head of main course = line of flotation × from .47 to .50.

Head of main-topsail = head of main course × about .7.

Head of main-topgallant sail = head of main course × about .5.

Head of fore course = head of main course.

Heads and depths of fore-topsail and fore-topgallant sails = as for main-topsail and main-topgallant sail.

Depth of royals = depth of topgallant sails × about .67.

Heads of royals = heads of courses × about .33.

The depth of canvas in a square sail is less than the depth from center to center of the yards between which it is set by about 1/30 of that depth.

BOWSPRIT MASTS AND YARDS

Height of hounds of lower masts above heads of courses = depth of topsails × about 1/8.

Projection of jibboom end beyond tack of jib = foot of jib × about .03.

Length of jibboom, 23 inches less than foot of jib.

Projection of outer end of bowsprit, beyond the heel of the jibboom = length of jibboom × about 1/3.

Heel of bowsprit steps in bowsprit partners before the foremast.

Flying jibboom = jibboom × from 1 to 1.2.

Projection of peak of gaff beyond peak of driver sail = head of driver × about .045.

Additional length of peak for displaying signals, from 3 to 6 feet.

Hounded length of topmast = depth of topsail, nearly.

Hounded length of topgallant mast = depth of topgallant sail, nearly.

Royal pole = topgallant hounded × about .7.

Skysail pole or signal pole = royal pole × about 1/3.

Length of each lower masthead = hounded length of topmast × about .3.

Length of each topgallant and royal yardarm = head of sail × about .05.

Each topsail yardarm = excess of half breadth of sail at the middle of its depth above half breadth at its head × 1/20 of the head of the sail.

Spritsail yard, across bowsprit = main-topsail yard.

Main-trysail gaff = main gaff × about .3.

Fore-trysail gaff = main gaff × about .5.

Swing booms, for feet of lower studding sails = lower yards × about .6.

The upper sails and yards of the two masts of a brig are made of equal dimensions in order that the spare spars and sails may answer to replace those of either mast.

A brigantine or hermaphrodite brig has the bowsprit and foremast of a brig and the mainmast of a schooner — each with its proper station, proportions, rig and sails. Some have square topsails on the main, like those of a double-topsail schooner.

These rules give an approximation that is safe to follow when in doubt.

An English authority gives the following dimensions of an American schooner, size not stated, apparently about 100 feet long, and probably about the year 1835.

	Extreme Length		Diam.
Mainmast	78′ - 9″	head 8′ - 0″	13½″
Main-topmast	26′ - 2″		7½″
Main-topmast pole	13′ - 1″		5 ″
Flag pole	6′ - 0″		2½″
Foremast	75′ - 9″	head 8′	21¼″
Fore-topmast	26′ - 2″		7½″
Fore-topgallant mast	13′ - 1″		5 ″
Flag pole	6′ - 0″		2½″
Fore yard	50′ - 0″	arm 2′ - 7″	11¼″
Topsail yard	33′ - 5″	arm 2′ - 7″	7½″
Topgallant sail yard	22′ - 2″	arm 1′ - 0″	4½″
Bowsprit	29′ - 0″		18 ″
Jibboom	37′ - 0″		11 ″
Main boom	50′ - 0″		11 ″
Main gaff	25′ - 0″	head 5′ - 0″	8½″
Fore gaff	25′ - 0″		8 ″
Square sail boom	45′ - 0″		9¾″
Square sail yard	22′ - 9″		5 ″
Lower swinging boom	22′ - 0″		4¾″
Lower swinging yard	11′ - 0″		2¾″
Fore-topmast studding sail boom	25′ - 0″		5¼″
Fore-topmast studding sail yard	14′ - 2″		3 ″
Topgallant mast studding sail boom	16′ - 9″		3¾″
Topgallant mast studding sail yard	10′ - 0″		2¼″

The American privateer *Herald*, of New York, built in 1813 by Christian Bergh, 230 tons [Am.], 101 feet on deck; 24 feet 8 inches beam; 10 feet 4 inches depth of hold; 18 guns; carried the following rig:

Mainmast, length 83 feet, head 9 feet, diameter 24 inches.

Foremast, length 80 feet, head 10 feet, diameter 24 inches.

Bowsprit, 18 feet outboard.

Jibboom, 32 feet long, diameter 9 inches.

Flying jibboom, 26 feet long, diameter 5½ inches.

Square sail yard, extreme length 58 feet, yardarms 1 foot 6 inches, diameter 9½ inches.

Square sail booms, 30 feet long, diameter 7 inches.

Jack yard for square sail, 25 feet long, diameter 7 inches.

Main boom, 52 feet long, diameter 12 inches.

Topsail yard, 36 feet long, yardarms, 12 inches, diameter 6 inches.

Topgallant yard, 25 feet long, yardarms, 12 inches, diameter 5 inches.

Fore-topmast, 28 feet long, head 4 feet, diameter 10 inches.

Main-topmast, 38 feet 6 inches long, head 14 feet, diameter 7 inches.

Gaffs, each 33 feet long, diameter 8 inches.

Studding sail yards (2), 14 feet 6 inches long, diameter 4 inches.

Studding sail yards (2), 9 feet 6 inches long, diameter 3½ inches.

Studding sail booms (4), 30 feet long, diameter 5 inches.

Sliding gunter or fore-topgallant mast, 34 feet long, head 16 feet, diameter 5½ inches.

Gaff topsail yard, 31 feet long, diameter 5 inches.

These spar dimensions were discovered by C. H. S. Snyder in the Public Archives of Canada and published in "Yachting." They are particularly valuable, as the *Herald* is so nearly the same size as H. M. schooner *Pictou*, in fact, it is highly probable that the *Pictou* is the *Herald*, renamed after her capture. The slight variations may be due to careless measurement. The rig, even if such is not the case, would approximate the *Pictou's* and the sail plan shows it reconstructed. It may be possible that other masting dimensions can be found that would fit the schooners that have been described, but when other data cannot be had, the proportions noted in Marestier, and comparisons with the spar dimensions of the vessels available in this book, as well as the masting rules of Fincham, will give sufficient data to reconstruct the rigs of any of the Baltimore Clippers.

Data on the rig of schooners during the Baltimore Clipper period is so difficult to find that the dimensions and spar measurements of H. M. schooner *Spider* of 1835, are here given. This vessel was apparently a sister ship of the two brig-schooners or brigantines, *Cockatrice*, and *Viper*, launched in

1831 from designs by Seppings. These vessels were designed for fast sailing, and were rather similar to the American type, but not at all extreme.

SPIDER

Length on deck	80 feet
Length of the keel for tonnage	64 feet, 5½ inches
Breadth for tonnage	23 feet
Extreme breadth	23 feet, 2 inches
Depth in hold	9 feet, 10 inches
Burthen in tons	182 89/94 tons
Draught of water, light forward	6 feet, 1 inch
Draught of water, aft	9 feet
Draught of water, load, forward	9 feet, 2 inches
Draught of water, load, aft	11 feet, 8 inches
Height of ports, fore	4 feet, 7 inches
Height of ports, amidships	3 feet, 5 inches
Height of ports, aft	3 feet, 7 inches

She carried 4 12-pounder carronades
2   6-pounder guns
6 guns.

Crew of 30 to 50 men.

Total weight of vessel fully equipped for foreign service, complete, 204 tons, 3 cwt.

	Yards	Inches	Diam. in Inches
Length of foremast	22	18	18⅞″
Length of mainmast	24	18	17¾″
Length of bowsprit	10	16	18½″
Length of jibboom	9	0	8⅛″
Fore-topmast, to the hounds	7	30	9¼″
Fore-topmast pole	3	32	9¼″
Fore-lower yard	18	12	10½″
Fore-topsail yard	11	6	7¼″
Fore-topgallant yard	7	6	4¼″
Fore gaff	8	26	6⅛″
Main-topmast, to hounds	8	18	7¼″
Main-topmast pole	2	3	7¼″
Main boom	17	18	12¼″
Main gaff	9	0	6¾″

Location of the masts: foremast, 1/5, and mainmast 20/31 of the length of the vessel on the load waterline.

For true length of lower masts add one inch per yard, as length given is to the shortheads; but as the vessel had longheads, the correction must be made.

The mainmast, for example, would be:

$$24 \text{ yds. } 18 \text{ in.} = 73' \text{-} 9''$$
$$24 \text{ inches} = + 2' \text{-} 0\frac{1}{2}'' \text{ about}$$
$$75' \text{-} 9\frac{1}{2}'' \text{ true length.}$$

Her sail dimensions were as follows:

Jib — 23′ foot × 38′ 6″ depth, area 592 square feet.

Fore gaff sail — 24′ head, 37′ foot, 39′ hoist, 53′ leech, area 1525 square feet.

Fore-topsail — 24′ head, 50′ foot, 26′ depth, area 962 square feet.

Fore-topgallant sail — 20′ head, 30′ foot, 10′ depth, area 250 square feet.

Fore-staysail — 30′ foot, 37′ depth, area 690 square feet.

Main gaff sail — 25′ 6″ head, 50′ foot, 43′ 6″ hoist, 59′ 6″ leech, area 1982 square feet.

Gaff topsail — 7′ head, 28′ foot, depths, 35′ and 22′, area 498 square feet.

Total area of plain sail 6499 square feet.

This rig approximates that given the Baltimore Clippers, but is rather on the short side. The *Spider's* sister ship, the *Cockatrice*, rigged as a brig-schooner, carried somewhat more sail, her sail area being around 7000 square feet. A Baltimore-built schooner 75 feet on deck, brig-schooner rig, carried 9083 square feet, including royals; without royals (on foremast only) she had 8854 square feet.

Proportions vary so much, however, that judgment must be used in reconstructing rigs, in spite of the general accuracy of Fincham's rules. The best method, generally speaking, is to use this rule and check by comparison with the spar dimensions of the various vessels given in this book.

The specifications of one of the Royal Navy schooners of this class, 80 feet on deck, 77′ 8″ rabbet to rabbet, on the load waterline, 64′ 5½″ on the keel, for tonnage, 23′ 3″ extreme breadth, 22′ 7″ moulded as for building, were as follows:

Deck ports, fore and aft, 2′ 6″.

Deck ports, deep, 2′ 1″.

Deck ports, sill from deck, 0′ 10″.

Main keel, elm, square amidships, 10″ x 12″.

Fore end sided, 8″ x 12″.

After end sided, 8″ x 12″.

False keel, elm, 6 inches thick.

Main keel, horizontal scarfs to be 3 feet long.

Diameter of bolts for scarfs, ⅞ inch.

Main stem, English oak, sided at the head, 1′ 1″ and to taper to the junction of the keel to 8 inches.

Stern post of English or African oak, sided at upper end, 11 inches at lower end (keel), 8 inches.

Inner post, fore and aft, at head, 7 inches.

Inner post, fore and aft, at heel, 12 inches.

Floors, sided, 8½ inches, moulded, 6¾ inches.

1st futtocks, sided, 8½ inches, moulded, 6¼ inches.

2nd futtocks, sided, 8 inches, moulded, 6 inches.

3rd futtocks, sided, 7½ inches, moulded, 5¾ inches.

Keelson, to square, 10 inches.

Bottom plank, 3 feet below light load line to rabbet, to be 2½ inches thick.

Main wales, English oak, 4 inches thick.

Deck beams, moulded, 7 inches.

Deck beams, sided, 8 inches.

Deck beams, to round up, 5½ inches.

Deck beams, flat, thick, 3 inches.

Deck, hook-sided, 7 inches, diameter of bolts ¾ inch.

Side planking, long lengths, 2½ inches thick, oak or pine.

These specifications would nearly suit a Baltimore Clipper of the same size, except as to materials, as pine and white oak would replace the English or African oaks used in the Royal Navy. This vessel, built to these specifications, were under the so-called "Scheme of Scantlings" in force at that time. They were perhaps a little heavier scantling than most of the Baltimore craft, but the difference would be slight, allowing for the changes in material and methods of seasoning. Very few of the Baltimore schooners had timbering treated as was the frame timbers in the Royal Navy; that is, seasoned in the salt ponds. American builders generally used air-seasoned timber, and generally these timbers were allowed to season in place in the ship's frame. This was not always true during the War of 1812, when vessels were launched with green timbers and, of course, such vessels had very short lives.

There does not seem to have been any rule for framing Baltimore schooners. Griffiths evolved a number of methods for timbering, but that was later than the Baltimore Clipper era. The builders seem to have had individual rules, and some made bad mistakes. The hogging of the *Ann McKim*, no doubt, was due to mistakes in framing. Generally speaking, it must be stated that the American builder, from 1800 to 1850, was singularly free from rules of construction, rigging, and design. He followed his bent, using comparisons, and his own experience and judgment as to proportions, for the vessel and her various parts. This makes it difficult to trace the construction details of Baltimore Clippers beyond those details shown in the plans that have been discovered. A casual study of the plans will indicate, however, that the frames and deck beams of Baltimore vessels were usually rather light. Their longitudinal strength depended on their keels, keelson, deadwood, planking and wales, rather than on clamps or fillers. The construction of the head was usually marked by extreme simplicity, but some that were built in New York and Boston, during the War of 1812, and also clippers built between 1820 and 1840, had trail boards, head rails and some carving. The majority had a plain gammon knee head. The smaller craft often had no head at all, merely a plain, curved stem as in the pilot boats, as has been noted. Reference to the various plans will often show the number and shape of the pieces comprising the stem and head.

The sterns varied. Some had square transoms and square tuck; others square transoms and round tuck. The last named were more common from 1808 on. These had the cross-seam at the intersection of the bottom of the transom and the rabbet on the stern post, which was strengthened by a heavy frame. This type of construction is still to be seen. The usual shapes of the transoms may be seen in the plans, which explain better than words.

The Baltimore Clipper did not, as a rule, have much freeboard, or sheer. This was a distinguishing mark in American vessels for many years, in fact, up to the time of the clipper ships. No reason, other than custom, seems to explain this feature. Of course lack of freeboard was something of an aid in sailing, but the high bulwarks common during the period very nearly counteracted the advantages gained.

Much has been written in the past on the raking masts of these craft. Probably no other reason for the extreme rake of their masts was considered other than custom. The position of the spars so far forward made rake of importance in the sharper vessels in overcoming pitching and diving. The trend of today in high narrow sails, with long masts, has brought forth many sailing craft with rake to their masts, some racing yachts having a great deal. The rake of the masts also aided the rigging of the vessel, and perhaps explains the light rigging so common in the Baltimore Clipper. Rake of masts was rather extreme in schooners up to about 1858, after which it was reduced until masts became nearly plumb. We are now beginning to see the rake again introduced. Undoubtedly raking masts have advantages that plumb masts lack, otherwise they would not keep reappearing. One thing can be said; it is easier to cut sails for vessels with masts raked. Their chief disadvantage is running off in light winds as the booms have a tendency to fall inboard and jibe.

There does not seem to have been many deck erections on Baltimore craft. They carried boats, of course. Privateers of about 85 feet carried three — cutter or whaler, gig and jolly boat. Some had two whalers, or one whaler and one launch. These had to be carried on deck; one small boat could be slung on davits over the stern. There were, however, no houses or deck galleys in use, with the possible exception of deck galleys on slavers, or in very small vessels for use in the West Indies.

The painting of the hull seems to have varied widely as yellow, black, green, and blue were used, with white or black bands. On privateers, the inside of the bulwarks were often painted red or brown, but the decks were usually bright. Yellow and black were popular colors, however, for pilot boats, in 1812-1814. They had yellow sides with black mouldings, wales, or trim. Very few were painted white, as it made them too prominent at a distance, which was considered naturally, a handicap during the war.

Marestier's data can be referred to for most of the factors of the design of the Baltimore Clippers. The only thing that is missing is the degree of deadrise. There does not seem to have been any stated rule for this, but the following list supplies a basis for comparison. The degree of deadrise has been taken from the mid-section, at the intersection of the rising floor and the rabbet. The readings were made from the horizontal, 90° being parallel to the centerline of the body plan. Vessels with hollow floors are given special reference, as will be seen.

	About	
Bermuda schooner, 1798	23° 30′ (R. N. schooner)	
Bermuda sloop (Chapman's)	25°	
Swift	28°	
Virginia-built privateer	25°	
Virginia pilot schooner	18°	hollow floor
Flying Fish	25°	
Dominica	27°	
Mosquidobit	28° 30′	
Pictou	27°	
Sealark	30°	
Alban	28°	
Grecian	24° 30′	
Hannibal, 1810 ship	22°	
Marestier's No. 3	28°	
Marestier's No. 6	25°	
Marestier's No. 7	25°	
Marestier's No. 9	25°	

About

Marestier's No. 12	26°
Marestier's No. 16	29°
Marestier's No. 17 (Virginia pilot boat)	15°
Marestier's No. 18	26°
Diligente	39° hollow floor
Fair Rosamond, about 1830	23°
Ann McKim	30° ⎤ These vessels did not
Bahama fruit schooner	26° ⎬ have stations vertical
New York pilot schooner, 1839	23° ⎦ to the rabbet.

In the majority of cases noted in this list the sections were taken vertical to the rabbet, and consequently some idea is obtained of the wide variation in rise of floor. In the Virginia pilot schooners the rise of floor is a little greater than the above indicates, as she has hollow floors, but low bilges. The *Diligente* has about 40° deadrise close to the keel, but due to the hollow her turn of the bilge is lower. The *Grecian* and *Fair Rosamond* have very little straight rise of floor, both being rather round on the bottom, which makes their actual deadrise greater than the figure given.

The consistency of Marestier's examples is noteworthy, from 25° to 26°, except with the shoal pilot schooners. The increase of deadrise is also noticeable in the latter boats. The *Diligente* is the most extreme, with 39°. The *Ann McKim*, with 30°, should be compared with the *Hannibal*, of 1810, with 22°. It would be rash, however, to say that these figures are more than approximate, so far as limiting the degree of deadrise in these craft is concerned, but 25° seems to be a fair average. Nor can a clear idea be had of the actual deadrise, of the examples noted, from the figures alone, as some of the vessels, the *Grecian* for example, had very slack bilges which made the real deadrise greater, as has been said, even though the measured rise of floor along the straight was less. However, in spite of these handicaps, the approximations indicate the trend of design. When it is considered that some of the later clipper ships had less than 10°, the rise of floor of the Baltimore Clipper was enormous.

In some of the later Baltimore models the idea of placing the greatest beam forward of the middle of the waterline length, was carried to extremes. The revenue cruiser in Marestier's examples is one of this class. The resistance would be increased due to the fact that such vessels became very bluff forward, but this was partially counteracted by the fact that such vessels usually had what was later called in naval architecture, "a raking midship section"; that is, the greatest beam on the various waterlines was not in one vertical plane, but rather in a sloping plane. The further down toward the keel the measurement was taken, the further aft the greatest beam was usually found. This was less marked in the sharper vessels, but is more or less obvious in all of the type. This same peculiarity often appears in fast sailing vessels of a much later date, some designers have made deliberate use of it.

The full deck outline, forward, was very common on American vessels up to the 1850's, the most extreme being the packet ships, but this was all above the water. At and below the load waterline, the vessels became very sharp. The Baltimore vessels, while not as extreme as the packet ships, were quite full at the deck, but the entrance, as a rule, was rather sharp at and below the load waterline. Of course in the extreme examples of greatest beam forward, the entrance was rather full and convex, but the majority of the Baltimore Clippers show a finer entrance than was common at their time, in fact, finer than is usually found in modern sailing yachts.

The overhang of the transom, that is, the distance the planking of the transom was abaft the rudder head, varied widely. The *Flying Fish*, the Virginia-built pilot boats and Marestier's Virginia pilot boat (No. 17), are at one extreme, while the other schooners shown in Marestier's plans are at the other. The pilot boat model privateers seem to be in between, and had moderate overhang. It might be deduced from this data that the stern overhang increased with the passing years, yet Mr. Lubbock's find, the *Fair Rosamond*, probably built in the 1820's, had almost no overhang aft, her rudder being just inside the transom, with no deck space aft of the rudder head. From this it would seem that the overhang cannot have had any regular evolution, but probably varied with the builder's eye for appearance and beauty.

The position of the boats on the Baltimore Clipper has been mentioned, and it is probable that the davits and gallow frames for carrying them on deck, varied in each vessel. A model of a clipper brig in the Dunkirk museum, marked as an American Opium Clipper, shows two large boats between the main- and foremasts, one over the other, and a small gig on stern davits over the transom. The davits are a continuation of the sheer, by the way. This model, fully rigged, has less rake to the bow than the *Diligente*, a different shaped head, and more sheer, judging from a photograph. It is probable that this vessel is intended for the *Antelope*, the only brig-rigged opium clipper built in America. She measured 370 tons and was built at East Boston, by Samuel Hall, for Russell & Co. She was a favorite vessel and was the only square-rigged vessel that could beat up the Formosa Channel against the northeast monsoon. Both the vessel and her captain, Philip Dumaresq, were so well liked that no vessel would be unloaded or refitted in the opium ports, until the *Antelope* had been taken care of.

In the Appendix to this volume will be found tables of proportions taken from Fincham's "Masting and Rigging." By referring to these tables, certain questions that arose in connection with the foregoing reconstructions may be better pointed out.

In the reconstruction of the *Flying Fish* and the *Bermudian* (three-masted schooner rig) the rule worked splendidly until the question of topmasts was reached. Fincham states that the main-topmast = beam × .25, but this is far too short and hardly equals the head of the mainmast. Evidently this is an error so the constant was changed to .95, arbitrarily, for no other reason than that this gave a result that compared favorably with the other examples. Usually the topmasts were equal to the beam, but as these vessels were more tender, the height was kept down somewhat. The error may be only in the edition of Fincham available to the writer. As no pictures of the *Bermudian* class are available, there are several other problems. The main-topsail yard, on the three-masted schooner, given as square sail yard × .607. As no main gaff is given, it leaves the question as to what spar is referred to. In drawing the sail plan, the writer concluded that the main gaff was the spar described erroneously as the main-topsail yard and proceeded accordingly. The main gaff existed, no doubt, as the fore gaff is taken from it, as well as the mizzen or driver gaff. As the application of the other proportions given in Fincham work out quite well, the difficulty arising in connection with the three-masted schooner rig is all the more surprising. The notes on the reconstruction of this rig are given in order to explain the drawing. The dimensions of the spars arrived at through the corrections noted, are as follows:

	Feet
Mainmast, hounded	60.05
Mainmast, headed	6.
Foremast, hounded	57.05
Foremast, headed	5.71
Mizzenmast, hounded	44.44
Mizzenmast, headed	4.44
Main-topmast, hounded	24.80 (beam X .95)
Main-topmast, pole	7.69
Fore-topmast, hounded	22.72
Fore-topmast, headed	7.04
Mizzen-topmast, hounded	22.22
Mizzen-topmast, pole	4.79
Bowsprit	19.97
Fore yard	39.35
Fore-topsail yard	27.55
Fore-topgallant yard	18.89
Square sail yard	39.35 (fore yard?)

	Feet	
Main-topsail yard	23.9	(main gaff?)
Main boom	17.79	
Fore gaff	25.33	
Mizzen gaff	21.51	
Driver boom	30.69	
Jibboom	19.37	
Flying jibboom before jibboom	7.75	
Swinging boom	19.68	
Ringtail boom	16.53	
Squaresail boom	17.31	

These dimensions are not as complete as could be desired. One wonders as to studding sails. An approximation has been sketched in on the sail plan, but there is no authority to quote, beyond the fact that it is well known that all naval sailing craft seems to have carried them. On inspecting the finished sail plan, the mainsail looks rather awkward. In the Bermuda three-masted leg-of-mutton schooners the mainsail had no boom and overlapped the driver. This is a better looking sail plan and it is surprising that these three-masted schooners of the *Flying Fish* model did not also carry it. It seems that the schooners built in Bermuda, on this model, had changes made in their rigs at various times, but details are missing. The best that can be said for the sail plan of the three-masted schooners is that the result is fairly correct. More examples of this rig would be needed to make an accurate check. If a painting of this class could be found it would be a great help in identifying their spar dimensions, and visualizing the rig.

The reconstruction of the double topsail rig of the *Grecian* is taken from Fincham, based on Example 2, Bermuda Schooner, as this gives the longest spars. The mast heights appear to be too short, but this sail plan gives an accurate idea of the general arrangement of the rig. A comparison of the spar lengths of the reconstructed *Grecian* sail plan with that of the *Pictou*, as the privateer *Herald*, will show that Fincham's rules give a smaller rig than the American schooner usually carried. These rules, however, have an important advantage in that they give man-of-war practice between 1800 and 1850, for the R.N., at least.

The reconstructed sail plans, other than those just noted, were taken from the spar dimensions given on the original draughts, with one exception — the main-topsail yard. In the Royal Navy the lug topsail was usually used; in a few cases a jib-head topsail took its place. The Americans, however, had a kind of sliding gunter or jack yard topsail, that was nearly jib-headed, This is shown in Marestier's sail plans and in the *Pictou*, as the privateer *Herald*, sail plan reconstructed from the builder's spar dimensions. In most of these reconstructions the Royal Navy lug-headed topsail is shown, but this is not necessarily authoritative, for when these vessels were in American hands no doubt they had either jib-headed topsails, or the gunter type as noted. These topsails can be seen in the Marestier drawings.

The various speculations and observations that have been made here cannot be considered as final but are put forth as matters of personal opinion and perhaps as indications for future research. So little has been accomplished in matters of technical research on the Baltimore Clipper, that there are few points, either in her history or in her design, upon which we can seize as being absolutely final. The dearth of written matter has been commented upon and unfortunately there appear to be few models and even fewer plans of this type now available. It is undoubtedly true that some plans and models exist abroad. The difficulty lies in finding them. It is hoped that the progress that has been made in this volume may lead to the discovery of further data and ultimately to more certain knowledge concerning the evolution of this immensely interesting type of vessel.

APPENDIX

Tables of Length and Proportion of
Masts, Yards, Booms, etc., from *The
Masting of Ships, and Mast Making*,
by John Fincham, London, 1829

Proportions for Masts, Yards, Booms, &c. of Schooners.

Length. Breadth	Known Quantities.	Ketch.	Schooners. Three Masts.	Brig forward. 1 Ex.	Brig forward. 2 Ex.	Schooners. Common.	Bermuda. 1 Ex.	Bermuda. 2 Ex.
Schooner, three masts 78·7 ft. 21·6 ft, Ditto, brig for. Ex.1. 110·6 ft. 25·6 ft, Ditto ditto Ex.2. 102·5 ft. 25·8 ft, Ditto common ...... 90·0 ft. 24·0 ft, Ditto Bermuda Ex.1. 95·0 ft. 24·7 ft, Ditto ditto Ex.2. 94·7 ft. 24·0 ft.								
Main-mast hounded..............	Breadth	2,7	2.78	3.11	3.1	2.61	2.75	2.83
Main-mast headed	Hounded length	193	.1	.13	1.3	.12	.13	.13
Fore-mast hounded..............	Main-mast houn ed ..	—	.95	.734	.6'	.92	.97	.91
Fore-mast headed...............	Hounded length......	—	.1	.193	.193	.12	.13	.13
Mizen-mast hounded	Main-mast hounded ..	.7	.74	—	—	—	—	—
Mizen-mast headed	Hounded length......	.16	.1	—	—	—	—	—
Main-top-mast hounded..........	Breadth	1,4	.25	1.1	1.2	.83	1.0	.99
Main-top-mast pole.............	Hounded length......	.156	.31	.43	.43	.5	.5	.52
Fore-top-mast hounded	Main-top-mt. hounded		.92	1.08	1.2	1.0	.9	1.0
Fore-top-mast headed	Hounded length......		.31	.156	.156	.5	.5	.54
Mizen-top-mast hounded	Main-top-mt. hounded	.8	.9	—	—	—	—	—
Mizen-top-mast pole	Hounded length......	.16	.24	—	—	—	—	—
Fore-top-gallant-mast hounded ..	Breadth	.8	—	.77	.79	—	—	—
Fore-top-gallant-mast pole	Hounded length......	.66	—	.55	.55	—	—	—
Bowsprit	Fore-mast	.72	.35	.55	.7	.49	.45	.5
Fore-yard	Length	.68	.5	.575	.61	.572	.48	.56
Fore-top-sail-yard	Fore-yard	.7	.7	.736	.764	.71	.747	.585
Fore-top-gallant-yard	Ditto..........	.461	.48	.574	.66	.458	.483	.422
Fore royal-yard..............	Top-gallant-yard	—	.5	.8	.7	—	—	—
Square-sail-yard	Length	—	.607	.44	.57	.52	.44	.47
Main-top-sail-yard	Square-sail-yard	—	.75	.64	.77	.75	.64	
Main-top-gallant-yard	Ditto..........	—	.48	.46	.5	.48	46	
Main-boom	Length	—	.226	.586	.6	.7	.66	.68
Main-gaff	Boom	—	.586	.72	.53	.44	.48	
Fore-gaff	Main-gaff..........	—	1.06	1.0	1.0	.73	1.0	.10
Mizen-gaff..................	Ditto..........	—	.9	—	—	—	—	—
Mizen or driver-boom	Length	.44	.39	—	—	—	—	—
Cross-jack-yard	Fore-yard	.56	—	—	—	—	—	—
Mizen-top-sail-yard...........	Cross-jack-yard	.7	—	—	—	—	—	—
Jib-boom...................	Bowsprit	.6	.97	1.21	—	.87	1.3	1.2
Flying jib-boom, before jib-boom	Jib-boom	—	.4	.4	—	—	—	—
Swinging ditto	Fore-yard	—	.5	.68	.68	—	—	—
Ringtail ditto	Length	—	.21	—	—	—	—	—
Square-sail ditto	Ditto..........	—	.22	—	—	.4	.37	.44
Fore-gaff...................	Length	.4	—	—	—	—	—	—
Driver-gaff.................	Fore-gaff	.59	—	—	—	—	—	—
		before	abaft	abaft				
Main-mast from the middle	Length of water-line..	.11	.033	.11	.107	.046	.108	.084
Fore-mast before ditto	Ditto..........		.295	.3	.294	.338	.279	.31
Mizen-mast abaft ditto	Ditto..........	.395	.366	—	—	—	—	—
Main-mast to rake	In twelve feet........	12 in.	27 in.	33 in.	28 in.	24	24 in.	33 in.
Fore-mast ditto	Ditto..........		24 in.	28 in.	18 in.	15	16 in.	36 in
Mizen-mast ditto	Ditto..........	18 in.	30 in.	—	—	—	—	—
Bowsprit to stive	Ditto..........	36 in.	22 in.	36 in.	33 in.	34	24 in.	22 in.
Main-mast below the load-water-line	Breadth..........	.32	.227	.26	3	.26	.31	.31
Fore-mast ditto ditto		.3	.17	.22	.217	.22	.27	.21
Mizen-mast ditto ditto			.232	—	—	—	—	—
Centre of effort from the middle of the length of the water-line	Length on water-line	.042	.0065	.0163	.015	.02	.023	.025
Height of the centre of effort above the load-water-line	Breadth.......... ×	1.74	1.539	1.72	1.6	1.5	1.5	1.56
Area of sails..........	Area of load-water section ×	4.7	4.944	4.59	4.62	3.63	3.54	3.61
Moment of sails..........	Ditto.......... ×	172.5	164 4	204.	96.	138.0	128.6	132.5
Bowsprit housed from the fore part of the stem	Breath	.5	.32	.35	.407	.46	.449	.45
Difference of draught of water, excess aft		9 in.	36 in.	24 in.	28 in.	12 in.	24 in.	48 in,

Lengths of Lower-masts, Top-masts, Bowsprits, and Jib-booms.

Dimensions of Vessel. Breadth. (Feet)	BERMUDA SCHOONER — First Example Main-Mast Hounded	Headed	Fore-Mast Hounded	Headed	Main Top-mast Hounded	Pole	Fore Top-mast Hounded	Pole	Bowsprit	Jib-boom	Second Example Main-Mast Hounded	Headed	Fore-Mast Hounded	Headed	Main Top-mast Hounded	Pole	Fore Top-mast Hounded	Pole	Bowsprit	Jib-boom	COMMON SCHOONER Main-Mast Hounded	Headed	Fore-Mast Hounded	Headed	Main Top-mast Hounded	Pole	Fore Top-mast Hounded	Pole	Bowsprit	Jib-boom
12.0	33.0	4.3	32.0	4.2	12.2	6.1	11.0	5.5	14.4	17.8	34.0	4.4	30.9	4.1	11.9	6.2	11.9	6.4	15.4	18.5	31.3	3.7	28.8	3.4	10.0	5.0	10.0	5.0	14.1	12.3
12.5	34.4	4.4	33.3	4.3	12.7	6.3	11.4	5.7	15.0	18.6	35.4	4.6	32.2	4.3	12.4	6.4	12.4	6.7	16.1	19.3	32.6	3.9	30.0	3.6	10.4	5.2	10.4	5.2	14.7	12.8
13.0	35.7	4.5	34.7	4.5	13.2	6.6	11.9	5.9	15.6	19.3	36.8	4.6	33.5	4.5	12.9	6.7	12.9	6.9	16.7	20.1	33.9	4.1	31.2	3.7	10.8	5.4	10.8	5.4	15.3	13.3
13.5	37.1	4.6	36.0	4.7	13.7	6.8	12.4	6.2	16.2	20.0	38.2	4.8	34.8	4.6	13.4	6.9	13.4	7.2	17.4	20.8	35.2	4.3	32.4	3.9	11.3	5.6	11.3	5.6	15.9	13.8
14.0	38.5	4.8	37.3	4.8	14.2	7.1	12.8	6.4	16.8	20.8	39.6	4.9	36.1	4.8	13.9	7.2	13.9	7.5	18.0	21.0	36.5	4.3	33.6	4.0	11.7	5.8	11.7	5.8	16.5	14.3
14.5	39.9	4.9	38.7	5.0	14.7	7.4	13.3	6.6	17.4	21.5	41.0	5.1	37.3	5.0	14.4	7.7	14.4	7.7	18.6	22.0	37.8	4.5	34.7	4.2	12.1	6.0	12.1	6.0	17.1	14.8
15.0	41.2	5.1	40.0	5.2	15.3	7.6	13.7	6.9	18.0	22.3	42.4	5.3	38.6	5.1	14.8	7.4	14.8	8.0	19.3	23.2	39.0	4.6	36.0	4.2	12.5	6.3	12.5	6.3	17.6	15.3
15.5	42.6	5.4	41.3	5.4	15.8	7.9	14.2	7.1	18.6	22.3	43.8	5.5	39.9	5.3	15.3	8.0	15.3	8.3	19.9	23.8	40.4	4.8	37.2	4.5	12.9	6.5	12.9	6.5	18.2	15.9
16.0	44.0	5.5	42.7	5.5	16.3	8.1	14.6	7.3	19.1	23.6	45.2	5.6	41.2	5.5	15.8	8.3	15.8	8.5	20.6	24.7	41.7	5.1	38.4	4.7	13.3	6.7	13.3	6.7	18.8	16.4
16.5	45.4	5.7	44.0	5.7	16.8	8.4	15.1	7.5	19.7	24.5	46.7	5.8	42.5	5.7	16.3	8.5	16.3	8.7	21.2	25.4	43.1	5.2	39.6	4.9	13.8	6.8	13.8	6.8	19.4	16.9
17.0	46.7	5.9	45.4	5.8	17.3	8.6	15.5	7.8	20.3	24.6	47.5	5.9	43.5	5.9	16.8	8.7	16.8	9.0	21.9	26.1	44.5	5.4	40.8	5.0	14.2	7.1	14.2	7.1	20.0	17.4
17.5	48.1	6.1	46.7	6.0	17.8	8.9	16.0	8.0	20.9	25.2	49.1	6.1	44.5	6.0	17.3	9.0	17.3	9.2	22.5	26.7	45.7	5.6	42.0	5.2	15.0	7.3	15.0	7.3	20.7	17.9
18.0	49.5	6.2	48.0	6.1	18.3	9.1	16.5	8.2	21.5	26.0	50.6	6.3	46.3	6.4	18.3	9.3	18.3	9.5	23.2	27.5	47.0	5.6	43.2	5.2	15.4	7.5	15.4	7.5	21.2	18.4
18.5	50.9	6.4	49.3	6.3	18.8	9.4	16.9	8.4	22.1	26.7	52.3	6.4	47.6	6.6	18.3	9.6	18.8	9.8	23.8	28.2	48.3	5.8	44.5	5.5	15.8	7.7	15.8	7.7	21.8	18.9
19.0	52.2	6.5	50.7	6.5	19.3	9.7	17.4	8.6	22.7	27.5	53.6	6.7	48.9	6.8	19.3	9.8	19.3	10.1	24.5	28.9	49.6	5.9	45.6	5.6	16.2	7.9	16.2	7.9	22.3	19.4
19.5	53.6	6.7	52.0	6.6	19.8	9.8	17.8	8.9	23.2	28.5	55.2	6.8	50.2	6.9	19.8	10.0	19.8	10.2	25.1	29.5	50.9	6.1	46.8	5.8	16.7	8.1	16.7	8.1	22.9	20.0
20.0	55.0	6.9	53.3	6.8	20.3	10.1	18.3	9.2	24.0	29.7	56.7	7.0	51.5	7.0	20.3	10.3	20.3	10.5	25.7	30.2	52.3	6.3	48.0	5.9	16.7	8.3	16.7	8.3	23.5	20.5
20.5	56.4	7.0	54.7	6.9	20.8	10.4	18.8	9.4	24.5	30.4	58.0	7.1	52.8	7.2	20.8	10.5	20.8	10.8	26.4	31.2	53.6	6.4	49.2	6.1	17.1	8.5	17.1	8.5	24.1	21.0
21.0	57.7	7.2	56.0	7.1	21.4	10.7	19.2	9.6	25.1	31.2	59.5	7.3	54.1	7.4	21.3	10.8	21.3	11.1	27.0	32.4	54.9	6.6	50.4	6.2	17.5	8.6	17.5	8.6	24.7	21.5
21.5	59.1	7.4	57.3	7.3	21.9	10.9	19.7	9.8	25.6	31.2	60.8	7.5	55.4	7.6	21.8	11.0	21.8	11.3	27.7	33.1	56.1	6.7	51.6	6.4	17.9	8.8	17.9	8.8	25.3	22.0
22.0	60.5	7.5	58.7	7.5	22.4	11.2	20.1	10.1	26.2	32.7	62.3	7.6	56.7	7.9	22.3	11.3	22.3	11.6	28.3	33.4	57.4	6.9	52.8	6.5	18.4	9.0	18.4	9.0	25.9	22.5
22.5	61.9	7.6	60.0	7.7	22.9	11.4	20.6	10.3	26.8	33.4	63.7	7.8	58.0	8.1	22.8	11.8	22.8	12.1	29.0	34.0	58.7	7.0	54.0	6.7	18.8	9.2	18.8	9.2	26.5	23.0
23.0	63.2	7.9	61.3	7.9	23.4	11.7	21.0	10.5	27.3	34.1	65.1	7.9	59.3	8.3	23.3	12.0	23.3	12.3	29.6	35.6	60.0	7.2	55.2	6.9	19.2	9.4	19.2	9.4	27.1	23.5
23.5	64.6	8.0	62.7	8.0	23.9	12.0	21.5	10.7	28.0	34.9	66.5	8.0	60.5	8.4	23.8	12.1	23.8	12.4	30.2	36.0	61.3	7.3	56.4	6.9	19.6	9.6	19.6	9.6	27.6	24.0
24.0	66.0	8.6	64.0	8.3	24.4	12.2	21.9	10.9	28.5	35.6	67.8	8.3	61.8	8.6	24.1	12.5	24.1	12.9	30.9	36.9	62.6	7.5	57.6	7.3	20.0	9.8	20.0	9.8	28.2	24.6
24.5	67.4	8.7	65.3	8.5	24.9	12.5	22.4	11.2	29.1	36.4	69.2	9.0	63.1	8.5	24.6	12.6	24.6	13.1	31.5	37.5	63.9	7.7	58.7	7.7	20.5	10.0	20.5	10.0	28.8	25.1
25.0	68.7	8.9	66.7	8.7	25.4	12.7	22.9	11.4	30.4	37.1	70.7	9.2	64.8	8.7	24.8	12.9	24.8	13.1	32.2	38.6	65.2	7.2	60.0	7.8	20.8	10.4	20.8	10.4	29.4	25.6

RIGGED FORWARD AS A BRIG, AND AFT AS A SCHOONER.

First Example.

Breadth of Vessel.	Main-Mast Hounded.	Main-Mast Headed.	Fore-Mast Hounded.	Fore-Mast Headed.	Main-Top-Mast Hounded.	Main-Top-Mast Pole.	Fore-top-Mast Hounded.	Fore-top-Mast Headed.	Fore-top-gallant-Mast Hounded.	Fore-top-gallant-Mast Pole.	Bowsprit.	Jib-boom.
17.0	52.9	6.9	38.8	7.5	18.7	8.0	20.2	3.1	13.1	7.2	21.3	26.
17.5	54.4	7.1	39.9	7.7	19.2	8.3	20.8	3.2	13.5	7.4	22.0	27.
18.0	56.0	7.3	41.1	7.9	19.8	8.5	21.4	3.3	13.9	7.6	22.6	27.
18.5	57.5	7.5	42.2	8.1	20.3	8.7	22.0	3.4	14.2	7.8	23.2	28.
19.0	59.1	7.7	43.4	8.4	20.9	9.0	22.6	3.5	14.6	8.0	23.8	29.
19.5	60.6	7.9	44.5	8.6	21.4	9.2	23.2	3.6	15.0	8.2	24.5	30.
20.0	62.2	8.1	45.6	8.8	22.0	9.5	23.8	3.7	15.4	8.5	25.1	30.
20.5	63.7	8.3	46.8	9.0	22.5	9.7	24.3	3.8	15.8	8.7	25.7	31.
21.0	65.3	8.5	47.9	9.2	23.1	9.9	24.9	3.9	16.2	8.9	26.4	32.
21.5	66.0	8.7	49.1	9.5	23.6	10.2	25.5	4.0	16.5	9.1	27.0	33.
22.0	68.4	8.9	50.2	9.7	24.2	10.4	26.1	4.1	16.9	9.3	27.6	33.
22.5	70.0	9.1	51.4	9.9	24.7	10.7	26.7	4.2	17.3	9.5	28.2	34.
23.0	71.5	9.3	52.5	10.1	25.3	10.9	27.3	4.3	17.7	9.7	28.9	35.
23.5	73.1	9.5	53.6	10.3	25.8	11.1	27.9	4.3	18.1	9.9	29.5	36.
24.0	74.6	9.7	54.8	10.6	26.4	11.3	28.5	4.4	18.5	10.2	30.1	36.
24.5	76.2	9.9	55.9	10.8	26.9	11.6	29.1	4.5	18.9	10.4	30.7	37.
25.0	77.7	10.1	57.1	11.0	27.5	11.8	29.7	4.6	19.3	10.6	31.4	38.
25.5	79.3	10.3	58.2	11.2	28.0	12.0	30.3	4.7	19.7	10.8	32.0	39.
26.0	80.9	10.5	59.3	11.4	28.6	12.3	30.9	4.8	20.1	11.0	32.6	39.
26.5	82.4	10.7	60.5	11.7	29.1	12.5	31.5	4.9	20.4	11.2	33.2	40.
27.0	84.0	10.9	61.6	11.9	29.7	12.8	32.1	5.0	20.8	11.4	33.9	41.

Second Example.

Breadth of Vessel.	Main-Mast Hounded.	Main-Mast Headed.	Fore-Mast Hounded.	Fore-Mast Headed.	Main-Top-Mast Hounded.	Main-Top-Mast Pole.	Fore-Top-Mast Hounded.	Fore-Top-Mast Headed.	Fore-top-gallant Mast Hounded.	Fore-top-gallant Mast Pole.	Bowsprit.
17.0	52.7	6.8	32.1	6.2	20.4	8.8	24.5	3.8	13.4	7.4	22.5
17.5	54.0	7.0	33.1	6.4	21.0	9.0	25.2	3.9	13.8	7.6	23.2
18.0	55.8	7.2	34.4	6.6	21.6	9.3	25.9	4.0	14.2	7.8	23.8
18.5	57.3	7.4	35.0	6.7	22.2	9.5	26.6	4.1	14.6	8.0	24.5
19.0	58.9	7.6	35.9	6.9	22.8	9.8	27.4	4.3	15.0	8.2	25.1
19.5	60.4	7.8	36.9	7.1	23.4	10.1	28.1	4.4	15.4	8.5	25.8
20.0	62.0	8.1	37.8	7.2	24.0	10.3	28.8	4.5	15.8	8.7	26.5
20.5	63.5	8.3	38.8	7.5	24.6	10.6	29.5	4.6	16.2	8.9	27.1
21.0	65.1	8.5	39.7	7.7	25.2	10.8	30.2	4.7	16.6	9.1	27.8
21.5	66.6	8.7	40.6	7.8	25.8	11.1	31.0	4.8	17.0	9.3	28.5
22.0	68.2	8.9	41.6	8.0	26.4	11.3	31.7	5.0	17.4	9.5	29.1
22.5	69.7	9.1	42.5	8.2	27.0	11.6	32.4	5.1	17.8	9.8	29.8
23.0	71.3	9.3	43.5	8.4	27.6	11.9	33.1	5.3	18.2	10.0	30.4
23.5	72.8	9.5	44.4	8.6	28.2	12.1	33.8	5.4	18.6	10.2	31.1
24.0	74.4	9.7	45.4	8.8	28.8	12.4	34.6	5.5	19.0	10.4	31.8
24.5	75.9	9.9	46.3	8.9	29.4	12.6	35.3	5.6	19.4	10.6	32.4
25.0	77.5	10.1	47.3	9.1	30.0	12.9	36.0	5.7	19.8	10.9	33.1
25.5	79.0	10.3	48.2	9.3	30.6	13.1	36.7	5.8	20.1	11.1	33.7
26.0	80.6	10.5	49.2	9.5	31.2	13.4	37.4	5.9	20.5	11.3	34.4
26.5	82.1	10.7	50.1	9.7	31.8	13.7	38.2	6.0	20.9	11.5	35.1
27.0	83.7	10.9	51.0	9.8	32.4	13.9	38.9	6.1	21.3	11.7	35.7

Length of Booms, Gaffs, and Yards.

Length (feet)	BERMUDA — 1st Example: Main Boom	Gaff Main	Gaff Fore	Sq-sail-yard Main	Sq-sail-yard Fore	Top-sail-yard Main	Top-sail-yard Fore	Royal-yard Main	Royal-yard Fore	Square-sail boom	BERMUDA — 2nd Example: Main Boom	Gaff Main	Gaff Fore	Sq-sail-yard Main	Sq-sail-yard Fore	Top-sail-yard Main	Top-sail-yard Fore	Royal-yard Main	Royal-yard Fore	Square-sail boom	COMMON: Main boom	Gaff Main	Gaff Fore	Sq-sail-yard Main	Sq-sail-yard Fore	Top-sail-yard Main	Top-sail-yard Fore	Royal-yard Main	Royal-yard Fore	Square-sail boom
50	33.0	14.5	14.2	22.0	24.2	16.5	18.1	10.5	11.7	18.5	34.0	16.4	16.4	23.3	28.2	15.0	16.5	10.8	11.9	22.2	35.0	18.5	13.5	26.0	28.6	20.0	20.0	13.0	13.1	20.0
51	33.7	14.8	14.8	22.4	24.7	16.8	18.5	10.8	11.9	18.9	34.7	16.7	16.7	24.0	28.8	15.3	16.9	11.0	12.1	22.4	35.7	18.9	13.8	26.5	29.2	20.4	20.4	13.3	13.4	20.4
52	34.3	15.1	15.1	22.9	25.2	17.2	18.9	11.0	12.1	19.2	35.4	17.0	17.0	24.4	29.3	15.6	17.2	11.2	12.4	22.9	36.4	19.3	14.1	27.0	29.7	20.8	20.8	13.5	13.6	20.8
53	35.0	15.4	15.4	23.3	25.7	17.5	19.2	11.2	12.3	19.6	36.0	17.3	17.3	24.9	29.8	15.9	17.5	11.4	12.6	23.3	37.0	19.7	14.3	27.6	30.3	21.2	21.1	13.8	13.8	21.2
54	35.6	15.7	15.7	23.8	26.1	17.8	19.6	11.4	12.5	20.0	36.7	17.7	17.7	25.4	30.4	16.2	17.9	11.7	12.8	23.7	37.8	20.0	14.6	28.0	30.9	21.6	21.6	13.9	13.9	22.0
55	36.3	16.0	16.0	24.2	26.6	18.2	20.0	11.6	12.7	20.3	37.4	18.0	18.0	25.8	31.0	16.5	18.2	11.9	13.1	24.0	38.5	20.4	14.9	28.5	31.5	22.0	22.0	14.3	14.0	22.4
56	37.0	16.3	16.3	24.6	27.1	18.5	20.3	11.8	12.9	20.7	38.1	18.3	18.3	26.3	31.5	16.8	18.5	12.1	13.3	24.3	39.2	20.8	15.2	29.1	32.0	22.4	22.5	14.4	14.2	22.0
57	37.6	16.5	16.5	25.1	27.6	18.8	20.7	12.0	13.0	21.1	38.8	18.7	18.7	26.8	32.1	17.1	18.9	12.3	13.5	24.7	39.9	21.1	15.4	29.6	32.6	22.8	22.9	14.8	14.4	22.4
58	38.3	16.8	16.8	25.5	28.1	19.2	21.0	12.1	13.2	21.5	39.4	19.0	19.0	27.3	32.7	17.4	19.2	12.5	13.7	25.0	40.5	21.5	15.7	30.2	33.2	23.3	23.3	15.0	14.7	22.8
59	38.9	17.1	17.1	26.0	28.5	19.5	21.4	12.3	13.4	21.8	40.1	19.3	19.3	27.7	33.3	17.7	19.5	12.7	14.0	25.4	41.3	21.9	16.0	30.7	33.7	23.6	23.7	15.3	15.0	23.2
60	39.6	17.4	17.4	26.4	29.0	19.8	21.8	12.5	13.6	22.2	40.8	19.6	19.6	28.2	33.8	18.0	19.8	13.0	14.3	25.8	42.0	22.3	16.3	31.2	34.3	24.0	24.1	15.5	15.3	23.6
61	40.3	17.7	17.7	26.8	29.5	20.1	22.1	12.7	13.8	22.6	41.5	20.0	20.0	28.7	34.4	18.3	20.2	13.2	14.5	26.2	42.7	22.6	16.5	31.7	34.9	24.4	24.5	15.9	15.5	24.0
62	40.9	18.0	18.0	27.3	30.0	20.5	22.5	12.9	14.0	23.0	42.2	20.3	20.3	29.1	35.0	18.6	20.5	13.4	14.7	26.6	43.4	23.0	16.8	32.3	35.4	24.9	24.9	16.1	15.7	24.4
63	41.6	18.3	18.3	27.7	30.5	20.8	22.9	13.1	14.2	23.3	42.8	20.6	20.6	29.6	35.5	18.9	20.8	13.6	15.0	27.0	44.1	23.4	17.1	32.8	36.0	25.3	25.3	16.3	16.0	24.8
64	42.2	18.6	18.6	28.2	31.0	21.1	23.2	13.3	14.4	23.7	43.5	20.9	20.9	30.1	36.1	19.2	21.2	13.8	15.2	27.4	44.8	23.7	17.3	33.3	36.6	25.7	25.7	16.6	16.3	25.2
65	42.9	18.9	18.9	28.6	31.5	21.4	23.6	13.5	14.6	24.0	44.2	21.3	21.3	30.6	36.7	19.5	21.5	14.0	15.4	27.8	45.6	24.1	17.6	33.8	37.1	26.1	26.1	16.8	16.5	25.6
66	43.6	19.2	19.2	29.0	32.0	21.8	24.0	13.7	14.8	24.4	44.9	21.6	21.6	31.0	37.3	19.8	21.9	14.2	15.7	28.2	46.3	24.5	17.9	34.3	37.6	26.5	26.5	16.9	16.7	26.0
67	44.2	19.4	19.4	29.5	32.5	22.1	24.3	13.9	15.0	24.8	45.6	21.9	21.9	31.5	37.8	20.1	22.2	14.5	15.9	28.6	46.9	24.8	18.1	34.8	38.2	26.9	26.9	17.3	16.9	26.4
68	44.9	19.7	19.7	29.9	32.9	22.4	24.6	14.1	15.2	25.2	46.2	22.3	22.3	32.0	38.4	20.4	22.5	14.7	16.2	29.0	47.6	25.2	18.4	35.3	38.8	27.3	27.2	17.4	17.2	26.8
69	45.5	20.0	20.0	30.4	33.4	22.8	25.0	14.3	15.5	25.6	46.9	22.6	22.6	32.6	38.9	20.7	22.8	14.9	16.4	29.4	48.3	25.6	18.7	35.9	39.5	27.6	27.6	17.6	17.3	27.2
70	46.2	20.3	20.3	30.8	33.9	23.1	25.4	14.6	15.7	26.0	47.6	22.9	22.9	33.0	39.5	21.0	23.2	15.1	16.6	30.0	49.0	26.0	19.0	36.4	40.0	28.0	28.0	17.8	17.6	27.6
71	46.9	20.6	20.6	31.2	34.4	23.4	25.8	14.8	16.0	26.5	48.3	23.3	23.3	33.6	40.1	21.3	23.5	15.3	16.9	30.4	49.7	26.3	19.3	36.9	40.6	28.4	28.4	18.1	17.7	28.0
72	47.5	20.9	20.9	31.7	34.8	23.8	26.1	15.0	16.2	26.9	48.9	23.6	23.6	34.0	40.6	21.6	23.8	15.5	17.1	30.9	50.4	26.7	19.5	37.5	41.2	28.9	28.9	18.5	17.8	28.4
73	48.2	21.2	21.2	32.1	35.3	24.1	26.5	15.2	16.5	27.3	49.7	23.9	23.9	34.3	41.1	21.9	24.1	15.8	17.4	31.4	51.1	27.1	19.8	38.0	41.8	29.4	29.4	18.7	18.2	28.8
74	48.8	21.5	21.5	32.6	35.8	24.4	26.8	15.4	16.7	27.7	50.3	24.2	24.2	34.8	41.7	22.2	24.5	16.0	17.6	31.7	51.8	27.4	20.1	38.5	42.3	29.6	30.2	19.3	19.4	29.6

Length of Booms, Gaffs, and Yards. (Continued.)

Dimensions of Vessel	BERMUDA SCHOONERS																				COMMON SCHOONERS									
	1st Example.										2nd Example.																			
Length.	Main Boom.	Gaff.		Square-sail-yard.		Top-sail-yard.		Royal-yard.		Square-sail Boom.	Main Boom.	Gaff.		Square-sail-yard.		Top-sail-yard.		Royal-yard.		Square-sail Boom.	Main Boom.	Gaff.		Square-sail-yard.		Top-sail-yard.		Royal-yard.		Square-sail Boom.
feet.	feet.	Main. feet.	Fore. feet.	Main. feet.	Fore. feet.	Main. feet.	Fore. feet.	Main. feet.	Fore. feet.	feet.	feet.	Main. feet.	Fore. feet.	Main. feet.	Fore. feet.	Main. feet.	Fore. feet.	Main. feet.	Fore. feet.	feet.	feet.	Main. feet.	Fore. feet.	Main. feet.	Fore. feet.	Main. feet.	Fore. feet.	Main. feet.	Fore. feet.	feet.
75	49.5	21.8	21.8	33.0	36.3	24.8	27.2	15.8	17.4	27.4	51.6	24.5	24.5	35.4	42.3	22.6	24.8	16.2	17.8	33.0	52.5	27.8	20.3	39.0	42.9	30.0	30.6	19.5	19.7	30.0
76	50.2	22.1	22.1	33.4	36.8	25.1	27.6	16.0	17.6	28.0	51.7	24.9	24.9	35.7	42.9	22.9	25.1	16.4	18.1	33.4	53.2	28.3	20.5	39.5	43.5	30.4	31.0	19.8	19.9	30.4
77	50.8	22.4	22.4	33.9	37.3	25.4	27.9	16.2	17.8	28.4	52.4	25.2	25.2	36.2	43.4	23.2	25.5	16.6	18.3	33.9	53.9	28.6	20.8	40.0	44.0	31.0	31.4	20.0	20.2	30.8
78	51.5	22.6	22.6	34.3	37.7	25.7	28.3	16.5	18.0	28.8	53.0	25.5	25.5	36.7	44.0	23.5	25.8	16.9	18.5	34.3	54.3	28.9	21.1	40.6	44.6	31.2	31.8	20.3	20.5	31.2
79	52.1	22.9	22.9	34.8	38.2	26.1	28.8	16.7	18.4	29.2	53.7	25.9	25.9	37.1	44.5	23.8	26.1	17.1	18.8	34.8	55.0	29.3	21.4	41.1	45.2	31.6	32.3	20.7	20.8	31.6
80	52.8	23.2	23.2	35.2	38.7	26.4	29.0	16.9	18.6	29.5	54.4	26.2	26.2	37.2	45.1	24.1	26.5	17.3	19.0	35.0	55.6	29.7	21.6	41.6	45.8	32.0	32.7	20.8	21.0	32.0
81	53.5	23.5	23.5	35.6	39.2	26.7	29.4	17.1	18.8	29.9	55.1	26.5	26.5	38.1	45.7	24.4	26.8	17.5	19.3	35.5	56.7	30.0	21.9	42.1	46.3	32.4	33.1	21.1	21.3	32.4
82	54.1	23.8	23.8	36.1	39.7	27.0	29.7	17.3	19.0	30.2	55.7	26.8	26.8	38.5	46.3	24.7	27.1	17.7	19.5	36.1	56.7	30.4	22.0	42.6	46.9	32.8	33.5	21.6	21.5	32.8
83	54.8	24.1	24.1	36.5	40.2	27.4	30.1	17.5	19.2	30.6	56.5	27.2	27.2	39.0	46.8	25.0	27.5	18.0	19.7	36.5	57.4	30.8	22.3	43.2	47.5	33.2	33.9	21.8	21.8	33.2
84	55.4	24.4	24.4	37.0	40.6	27.7	30.5	17.7	19.5	31.0	57.1	27.5	27.5	39.4	47.4	25.3	27.5	18.2	20.0	37.0	58.1	31.2	22.7	43.7	48.0	33.6	34.3	21.8	22.0	33.6
85	56.1	24.7	24.7	37.4	41.1	28.0	30.8	17.9	19.7	31.3	57.5	27.8	27.8	39.9	47.9	25.6	28.0	18.4	20.2	37.4	59.5	31.5	23.0	44.2	48.6	34.0	34.7	22.1	22.3	34.0
86	56.8	25.0	25.0	37.8	41.6	28.4	31.1	18.1	19.9	31.9	58.5	28.1	28.1	40.3	48.5	25.9	28.4	18.6	20.4	37.8	60.2	31.9	23.3	44.7	49.2	34.4	35.1	22.4	22.6	34.4
87	57.4	25.3	25.3	38.3	42.1	28.7	31.6	18.4	20.2	32.3	59.2	28.5	28.5	40.9	49.0	26.2	28.8	18.8	20.6	38.3	60.9	32.3	23.6	45.2	49.8	34.8	35.5	22.6	22.8	34.8
88	58.1	25.5	25.5	38.7	42.6	29.0	31.9	18.6	20.4	32.5	59.9	28.8	28.8	41.4	49.6	26.8	29.2	19.0	20.9	38.7	61.6	32.6	23.8	45.8	50.3	35.2	35.9	22.8	23.1	35.2
89	58.7	25.8	25.8	39.2	43.1	29.4	32.3	18.8	20.7	32.9	60.5	29.1	29.1	41.8	50.2	26.8	29.4	19.2	21.1	39.2	62.3	33.0	24.1	46.3	50.9	35.6	36.3	23.1	23.4	35.6
90	59.4	26.1	26.1	39.6	43.6	29.7	32.6	19.0	21.0	33.3	61.2	29.5	29.5	42.3	50.8	27.1	29.8	19.4	21.4	39.6	63.0	33.4	24.4	46.8	51.5	36.0	36.7	23.4	23.6	36.0
91	60.1	26.4	26.4	40.0	44.0	30.0	33.0	19.2	21.1	33.6	61.6	29.8	29.8	42.8	51.3	27.4	30.1	19.7	21.6	40.0	63.7	33.7	24.7	47.3	52.0	36.4	37.1	23.7	23.9	36.4
92	60.7	26.7	26.7	40.5	44.5	30.3	33.4	19.4	21.3	34.0	62.6	30.1	30.1	43.2	51.9	27.7	30.4	19.9	21.9	40.5	64.4	34.1	24.9	47.8	52.6	36.8	37.6	23.9	24.2	36.8
93	61.4	27.0	27.0	40.9	45.0	30.7	33.7	19.6	21.6	34.5	63.3	30.4	30.4	43.7	52.4	28.0	30.8	20.1	22.1	40.9	65.1	34.5	25.2	48.4	53.2	37.2	38.0	24.2	24.4	37.2
94	62.0	27.3	27.3	41.4	45.5	31.0	34.1	19.8	21.8	34.5	63.7	30.8	30.8	44.2	53.0	28.3	31.1	20.3	22.4	41.4	65.5	34.9	25.4	48.9	53.8	37.6	38.4	24.4	24.7	37.6
95	62.7	27.6	27.6	41.8	46.0	31.3	34.5	20.0	22.0	35.0	64.6	31.1	31.1	44.6	53.5	28.6	31.4	20.5	22.6	41.8	66.5	35.2	25.7	49.4	54.3	38.0	38.8	24.7	24.9	38.0
96	63.4	27.9	27.9	42.2	46.5	31.7	34.8	20.2	22.3	36.4	65.3	31.4	31.4	45.1	54.1	28.9	31.8	20.7	22.9	42.2	67.3	35.6	26.0	49.9	54.9	38.4	39.2	25.0	25.2	38.4
97	64.0	28.2	28.2	42.7	46.9	32.0	35.2	20.5	22.5	36.8	65.8	31.8	31.8	45.4	54.7	29.2	32.1	21.0	23.1	42.7	67.9	36.0	26.3	50.4	55.4	38.8	39.6	25.2	25.5	38.8
98	64.7	28.4	28.4	43.1	47.4	32.5	35.5	20.7	22.8	37.4	66.6	32.1	32.1	46.1	55.3	29.5	32.5	21.2	23.3	43.1	68.6	36.3	26.5	51.0	56.1	39.2	40.0	25.5	25.7	39.2

APPENDIX

Rigged as Brig Forward and Schooner Aft.

FIRST EXAMPLE.

Length of Vessel.	Main Boom.	Gaffs.		Fore-yards.				Main-yards.			Swing Boom.
		Main.	Fore.	Lower.	Top-sail.	Top-gallant.	Royal.	Square-sail.	Top-sail.	Top-gallant.	
feet	feet.	feet.	feet.	feet.	feet.	feet.	feet.	feet.	feet.	feet.	feet.
60	35. 16	20. 25	20. 25	34. 5	25. 39	14. 57	11. 65	26. 4	19. 8	12. 67	23. 46
61	35. 74	20. 58	20. 58	35. 07	25. 81	14. 81	11. 84	26. 84	20. 13	12. 88	23. 85
62	36. 33	20. 92	20. 92	35. 65	26. 23	15. 05	12. 04	27. 28	20. 46	13. 09	24. 24
63	36. 91	21. 26	21. 26	36. 22	26. 66	15. 29	12. 23	27. 72	20. 79	13. 3	24. 63
64	37. 5	21. 59	21. 59	36. 8	27. 08	15. 54	12. 42	28. 16	21. 12	13. 51	25. 02
65	38. 09	21. 93	21. 93	37. 37	27. 5	15. 78	12. 62	28. 60	21. 45	13. 72	25. 41
66	38. 67	22. 27	22. 27	37. 95	27. 93	16. 02	12. 81	29. 04	21. 78	13. 93	25. 8
67	39. 26	22. 6	22. 6	38. 52	28. 35	16. 26	13. 0	29. 48	22. 11	14. 14	26. 19
68	39. 84	22. 94	22. 94	39. 1	28. 77	16. 5	13. 2	29. 92	22. 44	14. 36	26. 58
69	40. 43	23. 28	23. 28	39. 67	29. 19	16. 75	13. 39	30. 36	22. 77	14. 57	26. 97
70	41. 02	23. 62	23. 62	40. 25	29. 62	16. 99	13. 58	30. 80	23. 1	14. 78	27. 37
71	41. 6	23. 95	23. 95	40. 82	30. 04	17. 23	13. 77	31. 24	23. 43	14. 99	27. 76
72	42. 19	24. 29	24. 29	41. 4	30. 46	17. 47	13. 97	31. 68	23. 76	15. 2	28. 15
73	42. 77	24. 63	24. 63	41. 97	30. 89	17. 71	14. 16	32. 12	24. 09	15. 41	28. 54
74	43. 36	24. 96	24. 96	42. 55	31. 31	17. 96	14. 35	32. 56	24. 42	15. 62	28. 93
75	43. 95	25. 3	25. 3	43. 12	31. 73	18. 2	14. 55	33. 0	24. 75	15. 83	29. 32
76	44. 53	25. 64	25. 64	43. 7	32. 16	18. 44	14. 74	33. 44	25. 08	16. 04	29. 71
77	45. 12	25. 97	25. 97	44. 27	32. 58	18. 68	14. 93	33. 88	25. 41	16. 25	30. 1
78	45. 7	26. 31	26. 31	44. 85	33. 0	18. 92	15. 13	34. 32	25. 74	16. 47	30. 49
79	46. 29	26. 65	26. 65	45. 42	33. 42	19. 17	15. 32	34. 76	26. 07	16. 68	30. 88
80	46. 88	26. 99	26. 99	46. 0	33. 85	19. 41	15. 51	35. 2	26. 4	16. 89	31. 28
81	47. 46	27. 32	27. 32	46. 57	34. 27	19. 65	15. 7	35. 64	26. 73	17. 1	31. 67
82	48. 05	27. 66	27. 66	47. 15	34. 69	19. 89	15. 9	36. 08	27. 06	17. 31	32. 06
83	48. 63	28. 0	28. 0	47. 72	35. 12	20. 13	16. 09	36. 52	27. 39	17. 52	32. 45
84	49. 22	28. 33	28. 33	48. 3	35. 54	20. 38	16. 28	36. 96	27. 72	17. 73	32. 84
85	49. 81	28. 67	28. 67	48. 87	35. 96	20. 62	16. 48	37. 4	28. 05	17. 94	33. 23
86	50. 39	29. 01	29. 01	49. 45	36. 39	20. 86	16. 67	37. 84	28. 38	18. 15	33. 62
87	50. 98	29. 34	29. 34	50. 02	36. 81	21. 1	16. 86	38. 28	28. 71	18. 36	34. 01
88	51. 56	29. 68	29. 68	50. 6	37. 23	21. 34	17. 06	38. 72	29. 04	18. 58	34. 4
89	52. 15	30. 02	30. 02	51. 17	37. 65	21. 59	17. 25	39. 16	29. 37	18. 79	34. 79
90	52. 74	30. 36	30. 36	51. 75	38. 08	21. 83	17. 44	39. 6	29. 7	19. 0	35. 19
91	53. 32	30. 69	30. 69	52. 32	38. 5	22. 07	17. 63	40. 04	30. 03	19. 21	35. 58
92	53. 91	31. 03	31. 03	52. 9	38. 92	22. 31	17. 83	40. 48	30. 36	19. 42	35. 97
93	54. 49	31. 37	31. 37	53. 47	39. 35	22. 55	18. 02	40. 92	30. 69	19. 63	36. 36
94	55. 08	31. 7	31. 7	54. 05	39. 77	22. 8	18. 21	41. 36	31. 02	19. 84	36. 75
95	55. 67	32. 04	32. 04	54. 62	40. 19	23. 04	18. 41	41. 8	31. 35	20. 05	37. 14
96	56. 25	32. 38	32. 38	55. 2	40. 62	23. 28	18. 6	42. 24	31. 68	20. 26	37. 53
97	56. 84	32. 71	32. 71	55. 77	41. 04	23. 52	18. 79	42. 68	32. 01	20. 47	37. 92
98	57. 42	33. 05	33. 05	56. 35	41. 46	23. 76	18. 9	43. 12	32. 34	20. 69	38. 31
99	58. 01	33. 39	33. 39	56. 92	41. 88	24. 01	19. 18	43. 56	32. 67	20. 9	38. 7
100	58. 6	33. 73	33. 73	57. 5	42. 31	24. 25	19. 37	44. 0	33. 0	21. 11	39. 1
101	59. 18	34. 06	34. 06	58. 07	42. 73	24. 47	19. 56	44. 44	33. 33	21. 32	39. 49
102	59. 77	34. 4	34. 4	58. 65	43. 15	24. 73	19. 76	44. 88	33. 66	21. 53	39. 88
103	60. 35	34. 74	34. 74	59. 22	43. 58	24. 97	19. 95	45. 32	33. 99	21. 74	40. 27
104	60. 94	35. 07	35. 07	59. 8	44. 0	25. 22	20. 14	45. 76	34. 30	21. 95	40. 66
105	61. 53	35. 41	35. 41	60. 37	44. 42	25. 46	20. 34	46. 2	34. 65	22. 16	41. 05
106	62. 11	35. 75	35. 75	60. 95	44. 85	25. 7	20. 53	46. 64	34. 98	22. 37	41. 44
107	62. 7	36. 08	36. 08	61. 52	45. 25	25. 94	20. 72	47. 08	35. 31	22. 58	41. 83
108	63. 28	36. 42	36. 42	62. 1	45. 67	26. 18	20. 92	47. 52	35. 64	22. 8	42. 22
109	63. 87	36. 76	36. 76	62. 67	46. 09	26. 43	21. 11	47. 96	35. 97	23. 01	42. 61
110	64. 46	37. 1	37. 1	63. 25	46. 52	26. 67	21. 3	48. 4	36. 3	23. 22	43. 01

Rigged as Brig Forward and Schooner Aft.

		SECOND EXAMPLE.									

Length of Vessel.	Main Boom.	Gaffs.		Fore-yards.				Main-yards.			Swing Boom.
		Main.	Fore.	Lower.	Top-sail.	Top-gallant.	Royal.	Square-sail.	Top-sail.	Top-gallant.	
44	36.0	21.24	21.24	30.0	22.92	15.12	10.58	28.2	18.05	12.97	20.4
45	36.6	21.59	21.59	30.5	23.3	15.37	10.76	28.67	18.35	13.18	20.74
46	37.2	21.94	21.94	31.0	23.68	15.63	10.93	29.14	18.65	13.4	21.08
47	37.8	22.3	22.3	31.5	24.06	15.88	11.11	29.61	18.95	13.62	21.42
48	38.4	22.65	22.65	32.0	24.44	16.13	11.28	30.08	19.25	13.83	21.76
49	39.0	23.01	23.01	32.5	24.83	16.38	11.46	30.55	19.55	14.05	22.1
50	39.6	23.36	23.36	33.0	25.21	16.63	11.64	31.02	19.85	14.26	22.44
51	40.2	23.71	23.71	33.5	25.59	16.89	11.81	31.49	20.15	14.48	22.76
52	40.8	24.04	24.04	34.0	25.97	17.14	11.99	31.96	20.45	14.7	23.12
53	41.4	24.42	24.42	34.5	26.35	17.39	12.16	32.43	20.75	14.91	23.46
54	42.0	24.78	24.78	35.0	26.74	17.64	12.34	32.9	21.05	15.13	23.8
55	42.6	25.13	25.13	35.5	27.12	17.89	12.52	33.37	21.35	15.34	24.14
56	43.2	25.48	25.48	36.0	27.5	18.15	12.69	33.84	21.65	15.56	24.48
57	43.8	25.84	25.84	36.5	27.88	18.4	12.87	34.31	21.95	15.78	24.82
58	44.4	26.19	26.19	37.0	28.26	18.65	13.04	34.78	22.25	15.99	25.16
59	45.0	26.55	26.55	37.5	28.65	18.9	13.22	35.25	22.55	16.21	25.5
60	45.6	26.9	26.9	38.0	29.03	19.15	13.4	35.72	22.85	16.42	25.84
61	46.2	27.25	27.25	38.5	29.41	19.41	13.57	36.19	23.15	16.64	26.18
62	46.8	27.61	27.61	39.0	29.79	19.66	13.75	36.66	23.45	16.36	26.52
63	47.4	27.96	27.96	39.5	30.17	19.91	13.92	37.13	23.75	17.07	26.86
64	48.0	28.32	28.32	40.0	30.56	20.16	14.1	37.6	24.05	17.29	27.2
65	48.6	28.67	28.67	40.5	30.94	20.41	14.28	38.07	24.35	17.5	27.54
66	49.2	29.02	29.02	41.0	31.32	20.67	14.45	38.54	24.65	17.72	27.88
67	49.8	29.38	29.38	41.5	31.7	20.92	14.63	39.01	24.95	17.94	28.22
68	50.4	29.73	29.73	42.0	32.08	21.17	14.8	39.48	25.25	18.15	28.56
69	51.0	30.09	30.09	42.5	32.47	21.42	14.98	39.95	25.55	18.37	28.9
70	51.6	30.44	30.44	43.0	32.85	21.67	15.16	40.42	25.85	18.58	29.24
71	52.2	30.79	30.79	43.5	33.23	21.93	15.33	40.89	26.15	18.8	29.58
72	52.8	31.15	31.15	44.0	33.61	22.18	15.51	41.36	26.45	19.02	29.92
73	53.4	31.5	31.5	44.5	33.99	22.43	15.68	41.83	26.75	19.23	30.26
74	54.0	31.86	31.86	45.0	34.38	22.68	15.86	42.3	27.05	19.45	30.6
75	54.6	32.21	32.21	45.5	34.76	22.93	16.04	42.77	27.35	19.66	30.94
76	55.2	32.56	32.56	46.0	35.14	23.19	16.21	43.24	27.65	19.88	31.28
77	55.8	32.92	32.92	46.5	35.52	23.44	16.39	43.71	27.95	20.1	31.62
78	56.4	33.27	33.27	47.0	35.9	23.69	16.56	44.18	28.25	20.31	31.96
79	57.0	33.63	33.63	47.5	36.29	23.94	16.74	44.65	28.55	20.53	32.3
80	57.6	33.98	33.98	48.0	36.67	24.19	16.92	45.12	28.85	20.74	32.64
81	58.2	34.33	34.33	48.5	37.05	24.45	17.09	45.59	29.15	20.96	32.98
82	58.8	34.69	34.69	49.0	37.43	24.7	17.27	46.06	29.45	21.18	33.32
83	59.4	35.04	35.04	49.5	37.81	24.95	17.44	46.53	29.75	21.39	33.66
84	60.0	35.4	35.4	50.0	38.2	25.2	17.62	47.0	30.05	21.61	34.0
85	60.6	35.75	35.75	50.5	38.58	25.45	17.8	47.47	30.35	21.82	34.34
86	61.2	36.1	36.1	51.0	38.96	25.71	17.97	47.94	30.65	22.04	34.68
87	61.8	36.46	36.46	51.5	39.34	25.96	18.15	48.41	30.95	22.26	35.02
88	62.4	36.81	36.81	52.0	39.72	26.21	18.32	48.88	31.25	22.47	35.36
89	63.0	37.17	37.17	52.5	40.11	26.46	18.5	49.35	31.55	22.69	35.7
90	63.6	37.52	37.52	53.0	40.49	26.71	18.68	49.82	31.85	22.9	36.04
91	64.2	37.87	37.87	53.5	40.87	26.97	18.85	50.29	32.15	23.12	36.38
92	64.8	38.23	38.23	54.0	41.25	27.22	19.03	50.76	32.45	23.34	36.72
93	65.4	38.58	38.58	54.5	41.63	27.44	19.2	51.23	32.75	23.55	37.06
94	66.0	38.94	38.94	55.0	42.02	27.72	19.39	51.7	33.05	23.77	37.4
95	66.6	39.30	39.28	55.5	42.02	28.1	19.56	52.2	33.3	24.0	37.8

INDEX

INDEX